abc's
of
INFRARED

D1374239

by
Burton Bernard

HOWARD W. SAMS & CO., INC.
THE BOBBS-MERRILL CO., INC.
INDIANAPOLIS · KANSAS CITY · NEW YORK

FIRST EDITION

FIRST PRINTING—1970

Library of Congress Catalog Card Number: 77-112863

PREFACE

The infrared spectrum was discovered 170 years ago but very little technical progress took place in the field for the first 130 years. The Second World War generated renewed interest in the infrared spectrum, and rapid advances in the state of the art have taken place. Today, infrared techniques are commonplace in domestic, industrial, military, medical, and space applications.

This book is an introduction to the theory and applications of infrared techniques. It may also be used as a refresher or reference for those already experienced in the expanding field of infrared technology.

Fundamental infrared physics and optics are discussed; this discussion leads to the design of basic infrared instruments and systems. Many applications are included, and typical examples and calculations are given with most equations. Multiple-choice questions are listed at the end of each chapter so that progress may be checked. The answers are given on p. 141.

BURTON BERNARD

ACKNOWLEDGMENTS

The author wishes to acknowledge the cooperation and assistance given by the following individuals: Herbert L. Berman; Paul R. Bradshaw; Arthur J. Cussen; R. Bruce Emmons; David L. Fain; Stuart D. Grandfield; Herbert S. Kaufman; and Erick M. Wormser.

Also, I wish to thank the following companies for permission to use their photographs: Barnes Engineering Company; Cintra, Inc.; Electro Optical Industries, Inc.; Exotech, Inc.; Infrared Industries, Inc.; OCLI, Inc.; Raytek, Inc.; and Sylvania Electric Products, Inc.

A personal and grateful thanks goes to Mrs. Raquel Santana for her endurance in typing, retyping, and proofreading every word of this book.

To Margie

CONTENTS

CHAPTER 6

CHAPTER 7

1

INTRODUCTION

All objects emit infrared radiation. Infrared energy is generated by the vibration and rotation of atoms and molecules within a substance. As an object becomes hotter, its molecular activity increases and causes that object to generate more energy. Only at absolute zero ($-273°C$), where all molecular activity stops, will an object cease to emit infrared radiation.

This page is emitting about 13.5 watts of infrared energy. The human body normally emits about 0.34 watt of infrared energy per square inch. The sun, whose absolute temperature is about 20 times that of the human body, emits over 100,000 times as much infrared energy per unit area. Over 50 percent of the sun's energy is emitted in the infrared region of the electromagnetic radiation spectrum.

Infrared energy plays an important role in our everyday lives. For example, infrared ovens may be used to cook meals or to dry paint; infrared cameras permit us to "see" in the dark, plot weather conditions from satellites, detect breast cancer, and predict electronic component failures; infrared techniques are used to guide missiles, remotely measure temperature, analyze the chemical composition of distant objects, alarm against unwanted intruders, and measure the amount and types of pollutants in the air we breathe.

Infrared technology combines the disciplines of optics with those of electronics. This book will explain the fundamentals of infrared energy and how it is generated, transmitted, and detected.

Chapter 2 deals with the basic infrared theory related to the emission, absorption, reflection, and transmission of infrared energy.

Chapter 3 discusses the fundamentals of optics and describes some optical properties, materials, and systems.

Chapter 4 is about infrared detectors, including their characteristics, theory of operation, and limitations.

The basic design and use of many types of infrared instruments are described in Chapter 5. Chapter 6 examines some of the many configurations that may be used for both active and passive infrared systems.

Typical infrared applications (including industrial, medical, military and space) are described in Chapter 7.

HISTORY OF INFRARED

Infrared radiation or energy was discovered in 1800 by Sir William Herschel while measuring the temperature of the various colors of the visible spectrum as separated by a prism. Herschel observed that the temperature of his thermometer increased as he moved it from the blue to the red. When he accidently placed his thermometer below the red region of the visible spectrum, he noted a further increase in temperature. Herschel called this invisible light *infrared,* meaning below the red (see Fig. 1-1).

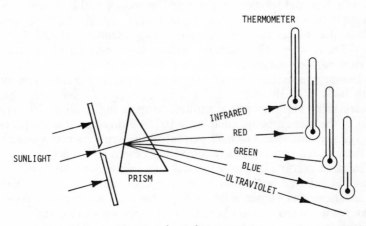

Fig. 1-1. Color and temperature.

It took over 100 years for the potential of infrared technology to be recognized. Recent developments of more sensitive, longer-wavelength infrared detectors, low-noise electronic amplifiers, and sophisticated optical systems are continually advancing the state of the art for infrared techniques.

Following is a list of chronological events that have lead to the advancement of infrared technology as we know it today.

Year	Discoverer and Event
50(?)	Lucius Annaeus Seneca—Discussed various topics related to physics and optics in his seven books of *Naturales Quaestiones*.
1025(?)	Alhazen—First to discuss the magnifying effect of a simple lens.
1609	Galileo Galilei—Used a refracting telescope; paved the way for use of optical systems for scientific investigations.
1621	Willebrord Snell—Discovered the law of refraction (Snell's Law, see Equation 3-2).
1666	Sir Isaac Newton—Studied the refraction of light through a prism. Built the first reflecting telescope (1668). Unfolded the fundamental properties of light (1669).
1676	O. Roemer—Calculated the velocity of light.
1669	Erasmus Bartholinus—First to observe the effects of polarized light.
1690	Christian Huygens—Advanced the theory of refraction based on the wave theory of light.
1729	James Bradley—Discovered aberrations in light.
1753	Thomas Melvill—Discovered that various chemicals emitted distinct colors when burned in an alcohol flame.
1758	John Dolland—Invented the achromatic lens.
1783	William H. Wollaston—First to use a slit for the study of solar spectral emission.
1800	Sir William Herschel—Discovered the infrared spectrum.
1801	J. W. Ritter—Discovered the ultraviolet spectrum.
1801	Thomas Young—Formulated the theory of color perception.
1810	Etienne Louis Malus—Presented the theory of double refraction.
1819	Augustin Jean Fresnel—Explained diffraction patterns by assuming light to be wave motion.

Year	Discoverer and Event
1822	Thomas Johann Seebeck—Discovered the thermoelectric effect.
1828	William Nicol—Invented a prism to produce polarized light.
1830	L. Nobile—Invented the thermocouple.
1833	Macedonio Melloni — Improved the thermocouple (thermopile). Made several important discoveries respecting the radiation of heat. Discovered that rock salt was transparent in the infrared.
1839	A. E. Becquerel—First to note the photovoltaic effect.
1845	Michael Faraday — Observed a relationship between magnetism and light.
1857	Jean Bernard Leon Foucault—Demonstrated that the velocity of light differs in different media.
1858	Gustav Robert Kirchhoff — Established that the absorbing ability of a surface is directly proportional to its radiating ability (Kirchhoff's law, see Equation 2-2).
1858	Gustav Robert Kirchhoff and Robert Wilhelm Eberhard von Bunsen—Developed the first practical spectroscope.
1868	Alexandre Edmond Becquerel — Demonstrated the phosphorescent and photographic effects of near-infrared radiation.
1872	John Tyndall — Measured the radiant power transferred by one heated body to another.
1873	James Clerk Maxwell—Presented the classical theory of electromagnetic radiation (based on Faraday's experiments).
1873	Willoughby Smith—Discovered optical photoconductivity in selenium.
1879	T. Stefan—Concluded that the rate at which heat is transferred from one body to another is proportional to the difference of the fourth power of their absolute temperatures.
1881	Samuel Pierpont Langley—Developed the bolometer.

Year	Discoverer and Event
1884	Ludwig Boltzmann—Showed theoretically that Stefan's law of radiation from a body was correct. (Stefan-Boltzmann constant, see Equation 2-5).
1886	Albert Abraham Michelson—Measured the velocity of light. Developed the interferometer.
1887	Heinrich Rudolph Hertz—Showed that there was essentially no difference between thermally and electrically produced electromagnetic waves.
1895	Julius Elster and Hans F. Geitel—Invented the photoelectric cell.
1900	Max Planck — Established the quantum theory in which radiant energy consists of discrete quantities of energy called *photons*.
1904	J. C. Bose—Announced the discovery of an infrared photovoltaic effect in lead sulfide.
1905	Albert Einstein — Explained the photoelectric effect. Contributed to the validity of the quantum theory.
1917	T. W. Case—Discovered that thallous sulfide was photosensitive in the infrared. Developed the "Thalofide cell" in 1920.
1919	S. O. Hoffman—Described one of the earliest passive infrared systems that could detect a man at 600 feet.
1919	A. O. Rankine—Described voice transmission by light.
1929	M. Czerny—Built the "evapograph," the first working infrared imaging device.
1929	L. R. Koller—Described the first infrared image tube.
1930	H. D. Babcock—Published the first all-infrared photograph.
1934	I. K. Nikion and M. M. Noskov—Discovered the photoelectromagnetic effect.
1940	G. Hass—Found that silicon monoxide could be used as a protective layer on front-surfaced mirrors.
1943	R. Koops and A. Smakula—Produced a mixed crystal that is transparent to 40 micrometers; called KRS-5.

Year	Discoverer and Event
1946	J. A. Becker and W. H. Brattain — Developed the thermistor bolometer.
1947	M. J. E. Golay—Built an improved pneumatic detector (golay cell).
1958	C. Townes and A. Schawlow—Described a device that could stimulate molecules of gas to emit photons.
1960	T. M. Maiman—Constructed the first operating laser.

ELECTROMAGNETIC RADIATION

Infrared radiation, like radio waves, light, ultraviolet, and x-ray radiation, is electromagnetic and travels through space at the speed of light. The difference between infrared radiation and other types of electromagnetic radiation is the wavelength of the electromagnetic wave (Fig. 1-2).

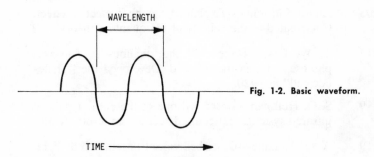

Fig. 1-2. Basic waveform.

Electromagnetic radiation is generally measured in wavelength or frequency. The relationship between wavelength and frequency is

$$\lambda = \frac{c}{f} \qquad (1\text{-}1)$$

where,
λ equals wavelength in meters,
c equals speed of light (3×10^8 meters per second),
f equals frequency in hertz (cycles per second).

Example—What is the wavelength of an electromagnetic wave travelling at 100 megahertz?

Answer—From Equation 1-1,

$$\lambda = \frac{3 \times 10^8 \text{ meters per second}}{10^8 \text{ hertz}}$$

$$= 3 \text{ meters}$$

The infrared spectrum consists of wavelengths shorter than those of radio waves and longer than those of light. The infrared portion of the electromagnetic radiation spectrum is generally measured in micrometers (10^{-6} meter). The symbol used for micrometer is μm.

NOTE: Prior to the adoption of the International System of Units by the National Bureau of Standards in 1964, the term *micron* and symbol μ were commonly used in place of micrometer (μm).

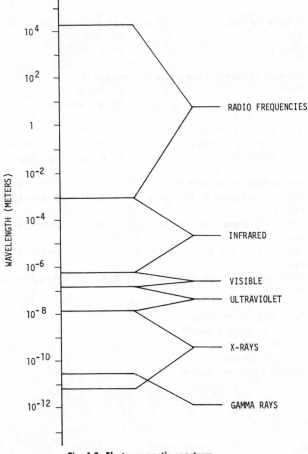

Fig. 1-3. Electromagnetic spectrum.

The infrared spectrum falls between 0.7 and 1000 micrometers (Fig. 1-3).

Another unit of measurement occasionally used for infrared wavelengths is the angstrom (Å). One angstrom equals 10^{-10} meter, or 10^{-4} micrometer.

QUESTIONS

1-1. Who discovered infrared radiation?
A. James Clerk Maxwell. C. Sir William Herschel.
B. Sir Isaac Newton. D. Ludwig Boltzmann.

1-2. In what year was infrared radiation discovered?
A. 1666. C. 1910.
B. 1800. D. 1852.

1-3. What is the correct relationship between wavelength and frequency?
A. $\lambda = 2\pi c/f$. C. $cf = \lambda$.
B. $f = \lambda/c$. D. $\lambda = c/f$.

1-4. Infrared wavelengths are normally measured in:
A. Hertz. C. Watts.
B. Ergs. D. Micrometers.

1-5. The infrared spectrum falls between which wavelengths?
A. 0.7 to 1000 micrometers. C. 10 to 100 micrometers.
B. 0.1 to 100 micrometers. D. 0.3 to 70 micrometers.

1-6. Which statement is correct?
A. Infrared is higher in frequency and lower in wavelength than visible radiation.
B. Infrared is higher in frequency and higher in wavelength than visible radiation.
C. Infrared is lower in frequency and lower in wavelength than visible radiation.
D. Infrared is lower in frequency and higher in wavelength than visible radiation.

1-7. What is the speed of light?
A. 3×10^8 meters per minute.
B. 3×10^9 meters per second.
C. 3×10^8 miles per second.
D. 8×10^3 meters per second.

2

INFRARED THEORY

Infrared radiation obeys many of the laws that apply to light. When infrared energy strikes an object it may be reflected from that surface, transmitted through the surface, or absorbed into that surface. Three terms are commonly used here:

Reflectivity (ρ) is a measure of an object's ability to reflect incident energy.

Absorptivity (α) is a measure of an object's ability to absorb incident energy.

Transmissivity (τ) is a measure of an object's ability to transmit incident energy.

Transmission, reflection, and absorption of infrared energy are shown in Fig. 2-1.

The sum of absorptivity, reflectivity, and transmissivity must equal 100 percent of the total incident energy, or

$$1 = \rho + \alpha + \tau \qquad (2\text{-}1)$$

where,

ρ equals reflectivity,
α equals absorptivity,
τ equals transmissivity.

Example—If infrared energy were to strike an object that is 20 percent reflective and 65 percent transparent then how much of the incident energy would be absorbed by that object?

Answer—From Equation 2-1,

$$1 = 0.20 + \alpha + 0.65$$

Transposing,

$$\alpha = 1 - (0.20 + 0.65) = 0.15 \text{ (or 15 percent)}$$

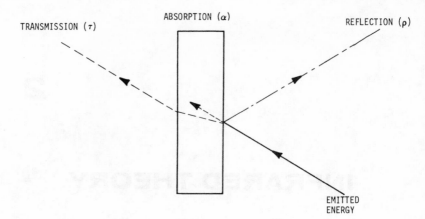

TRANSMISSION (τ)   ABSORPTION (α)   REFLECTION (ρ)

EMITTED
ENERGY

Fig. 2-1. Transmission, absorption, and reflection of infrared energy.

Some surfaces, such as mirrors, are excellent reflectors and do not transmit any radiation. A perfect mirror will have a reflectivity of 1.0 and therefore an absorptivity and transmissivity of 0. A perfect absorber will have an absorptivity of 1.0.

There are no perfect absorbers, reflectors, or transmitters found in nature.

An object that has zero transmissivity is said to be *opaque*.

FUNDAMENTALS

A perfect absorber is called a *blackbody*. A blackbody absorbs all of the radiation incident on it. Since it absorbs 100 percent of the incident energy, it has no reflectivity and no transmissivity. (Blackbody configurations will be discussed later in this chapter.) A blackbody is not only a perfect absorber but a perfect emitter as well: that is, it will emit the maximum amount of radiant energy at any given temperature. A low-temperature blackbody radiation source is shown in Fig. 2-2.

Kirchhoff's Law

According to Kirchhoff, when an object is at thermal equilibrium, the amount of absorption (or absorptivity, α) will equal the amount of emission (or emissivity, ϵ). This may be written as

$$\alpha = \epsilon \qquad (2-2)$$

and by substitution from Equation 2-1,

$$\epsilon = 1 - (\rho + \tau) \qquad (2-3)$$

Fig. 2-2. Blackbody radiation source.

Since absorption is the exact opposite of emission, it is sometimes difficult to understand why they are numerically equal at thermal equilibrium. This may be visualized by placing an object into an oven. At first the object will absorb radiation from the walls of the oven and begin to get warmer. Eventually the object will reach thermal equilibrium and maintain the temperature of the oven.

If the object absorbed more energy than it emitted it would become hotter than the oven. If the object emitted more energy than it absorbed it would never reach the oven temperature. We know that neither of these conditions is true. Therefore for a given surface at thermal equilibrium, emissivity numerically equals absorptivity.

Emissivity

Emissivity is a measure of the ability, or ease, at which an object, or surface, emits infrared radiation.

Emissivity is the ratio of the radiant energy emitted by an object at a temperature T and the radiant energy emitted by a blackbody at the same temperature T. This may be written as

$$\epsilon = \frac{W_o}{W_{bb}} \qquad (2\text{-}4)$$

where,

W_o equals total radiant energy emitted by an object at a given temperature T,

W_{bb} equals total radiant energy emitted by a blackbody at the same temperature T.

Example—A cast-iron pipe at 200°C is emitting 0.21 watt of power. A blackbody at 200°C will emit 0.28 watt of energy. What is the emissivity value of the cast-iron pipe?

Answer—From Equation 2-4,

$$\epsilon = \frac{0.21}{0.28} = \frac{3}{4} = 0.75$$

Emissivity values may vary between 0 (for perfect reflector or perfect transmitter) to 1.0 for a blackbody. Some typical emissivity factors are listed in Table 2-1.

Table 2-1. Typical Emissivity Values

Materials	Emissivity
Aluminum	0.05
Carbon	0.81
Cotton Cloth	0.77
Gold	0.02
Paper	0.75
Plaster	0.92
Sand	0.76
Silver	0.02
Wood	0.89

Stefan-Boltzmann Law

The hotter an object becomes, the more infrared energy it emits. The following formula shows the relationship between the total energy emitted by an object and its temperature:

$$W = \epsilon \sigma T^4 \tag{2-5}$$

where,

W equals radiant energy in watts per square centimeter,
ϵ equals emissivity factor,
σ equals Stefan-Boltzmann constant (5.67×10^{-12} W/cm^{2}K^4),
T equals temperature in kelvins.

Example 1—How much infrared energy will be emitted by an object having an emissivity factor of 0.5 at a temperature of 1000 kelvins?

Answer—From Equation 2-5,

$$W = \frac{0.5\,(5.67 \times 10^{-12}\,\text{W})\,1000^4\,\text{K}^4}{\text{cm}^2\,\text{K}^4}$$

$$= \frac{0.5\,(5.67 \times 10^{-12}\text{W})\,10^{12}}{\text{cm}^2}$$

$$= 2.835 \text{ W/cm}^2$$

Table 2-2. Other Values of Stefan-Boltzmann Constant

5.672×10^{-12} W cm^{-2} K^{-4}
5.672×10^{-5} erg s^{-1} cm^{-2} K^{-4}
1.7×10^{-8} Btu ft^{-2} hr^{-1} deg R^{-4}
5.672×10^{-8} J s^{-1} m^{-2} K^{-4}

Example 2—How much infrared energy will be emitted by a blackbody at a temperature of 427° Celsius? (NOTE: 0° Celsius equals 273 kelvins.)

Answer—From Equation 2-5,

$$W = \frac{1.0\ (5.67 \times 10^{-12}\text{W})\ 700^4 \text{K}^4}{\text{cm}^2\ \text{K}^4}$$

$$= \frac{(5.67 \times 10^{-12}\ \text{W})\ 2.4 \times 10^{11}}{\text{cm}^2}$$

$$= 1.36\ \text{W/cm}^2$$

Table 2-2 gives other equivalent values of the Stefan-Boltzmann constant. Fig. 2-3 shows the radiant energy of a blackbody as a function of temperature. Table 2-3 shows some common temperatures and their equivalents.

If two objects are placed near each other, then the amount of radiant energy emitted from the hotter object to the cooler object is pro-

Table 2-3. Temperature Conversion Scale

	Kelvin (K)	Celsius (°C)	Fahrenheit (°F)	Rankine (°R)
Absolute Zero	0	−273	−460	0
Liquid Helium	4	−269	−452	8
Liquid Hydrogen	32	−241	−402	58
Liquid Oxygen	155	−118	−180	280
Mercury*	234	−39	−38	422
Water Freezes	273	0	32	492
Human Body	310	37	99	559
Water Boils	373	100	212	672
Lead*	600	327	621	1081
Aluminum*	930	657	1214	1674
Silver*	1233	960	1760	2220
Gold*	1336	1063	1945	2405
Iron*	1808	1535	2795	3255
Tungsten*	3643	3370	6098	6558
Sun's Surface	≃5773	≃5500	≃10000	≃10460

* Melting Point.

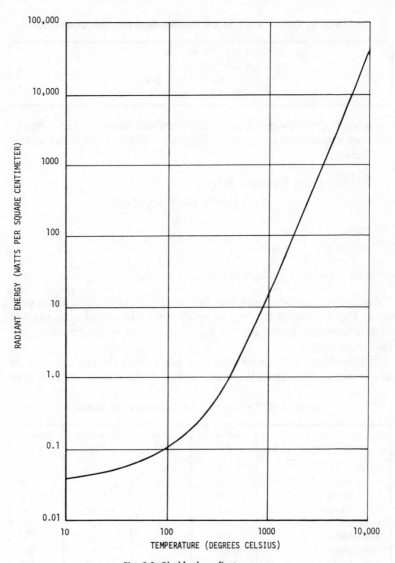

Fig. 2-3. Blackbody radiant energy.

portional to the difference of the fourth power of their absolute temperatures. Mathematically, this may be shown as

$$W = \epsilon\sigma(T_1{}^4 - T_2{}^4) \qquad (2\text{-}6)$$

where,

T_1 equals temperature of the hotter object in kelvins,

T_2 equals temperature of the cooler object in kelvins.

Example—If object 1 is at 800 K and object 2 is at 600 K, then how much energy will be radiated from object 1 to object 2, assuming ϵ to equal 0.5 for both objects?

Answer—From Equation 2-6,

$$W = \frac{0.5 \ (5.67 \times 10^{-12} \ \text{W})}{\text{cm}^2 \ \text{K}^4} \ [(800 \ \text{K})^4 - (600 \ \text{K})^4]$$

$$W = \frac{2.835 \times 10^{-12} \ \text{W}}{\text{cm}^2} \ (4.096 \times 10^{11} - 1.296 \times 10^{11})$$

$$W = \frac{2.835 \times 10^{-12} \ \text{W}}{\text{cm}^2} \ (2.8 \times 10^{11}) = 0.79 \ \text{W/cm}^2$$

The radiant energy of an object is emitted at many wavelengths. The amount of energy emitted at any given wavelength increases as the temperature increases.

Wien's Displacement Law

The wavelength at which the maximum amount of energy is emitted becomes shorter as the temperature is increased (Fig. 2-4). Mathematically,

$$\lambda_{max} = 2.89 \times 10^3 \ \mu\text{m K}/T \qquad (2\text{-}7)$$

where,

λ_{max} equals maximum wavelength in micrometers,
T equals temperature in kelvins.

Example—At what wavelength will the maximum amount of energy be emitted from a 2617° Celsius source?

Answer—Observe that 2617° Celsius + 273° = 2890 kelvins, so

$$\lambda_{max} = \frac{2.89 \times 10^3 \ \mu\text{m K}}{2.89 \times 10^3 \ \text{K}} = 1.0 \ \mu\text{m}$$

It should be mentioned at this time that we have been discussing total radiation emitted by an object: that is, radiation emitted at many wavelengths and following the same pattern as shown in Fig. 2-4.

An object that emits energy distributed as shown in Fig. 2-4 is a blackbody (if the total emissivity is equal to 1.0) or a graybody (if the total emissivity is less than 1.0).

The emissivity value for a blackbody or a graybody is the same for all wavelengths. About 25 percent of the total energy emitted by a blackbody or a graybody source is at wavelengths shorter than the wavelength of maximum energy.

Spectral emissivity is the emissivity value of an object for a given wavelength ϵ_λ or wavelength interval ($\epsilon_{\lambda_1 - \lambda_2}$).

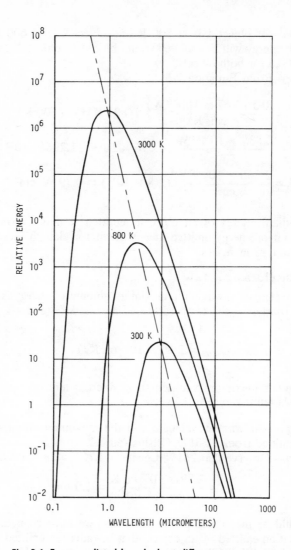

Fig. 2-4. Energy radiated by a body at different temperatures.

Most materials have different spectral emissivity characteristics, as can be seen in Fig. 2-5. It should be pointed out, however, that, for some materials, emissivity may also vary with temperature, as can be seen in Fig. 2-6.

Planck's Equation

The relationship between spectral emissivity, temperature, and radiant energy is given by Planck's equation:

$$W_\lambda = \frac{\epsilon_\lambda c_1}{\lambda^5 \left(e^{c2/\lambda T} - 1\right)} \tag{2-8}$$

where,

W_λ equals radiation emitted by an object at a given wavelength (λ),
ϵ_λ equals emissivity of the object at the same wavelength (λ),
c_1 equals Planck's first radiation constant (3.75×10^{-12} W cm^2),
c_2 equals Planck's second radiation constant (1.438 cm K),
λ equals wavelength in micrometers,
e equals base of natural logarithms (2.718),
T equals temperature in kelvins.

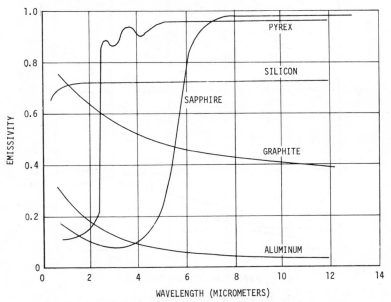

Fig. 2-5. Spectral emissivities of various materials.

Lambert's Law

The amount of radiant energy from a given surface varies with the cosine of the angle from which it leaves that surface (Fig. 2-7):

$$W_\theta = W \cos \theta \tag{2-9}$$

where,

W_θ equals energy emitted at angle θ,
W equals energy emitted at the normal (right angle) to the surface ($\theta = 0°$),
θ equals angle between the direction of energy being emitted and the normal (right angle) of the surface from which the energy is being emitted.

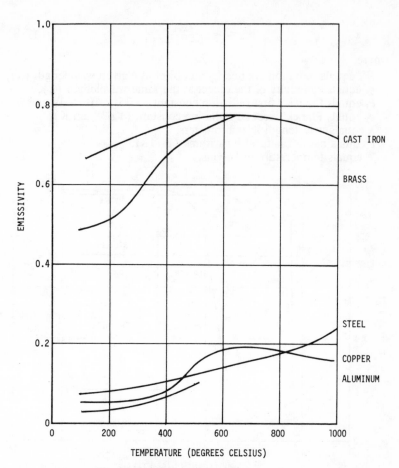

Fig. 2-6. Emissivity variation with temperature.

Example—If a surface normally emits 24 watts of energy at a right angle to its surface, then how much energy will be emitted at an angle of: (a) 45°, (b) 60°?

Answer—From Equation 2-9,

(a) $W_\theta = 24$ watts cos 45°
    $= 24 \times 0.707 = 16.9$ watts

(b) $W_\theta = 24$ watts cos 60°
    $= 24 \times 0.5 = 12$ watts

Equations 2-4 (Stefan-Boltzmann law) and 2-8 (Planck's equation) are for the total amount of energy emitted by a surface (of a given area) into a solid angle of 2π steradians (the total hemisphere of space surrounding that surface).

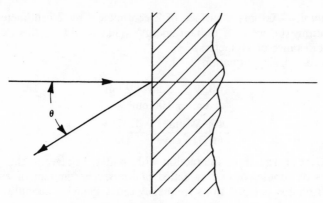

Fig. 2-7. Angle of radiation.

The intensity of radiation (I) emitted by a surface is the radiant energy per steradian normal to the surface, or

$$I = \frac{W}{\pi} \qquad (2\text{-}10)$$

and by substitution from Equation 2-5,

$$I = \frac{\epsilon \sigma T^4}{\pi} \qquad (2\text{-}11)$$

Inverse Square Law

The intensity of radiation emitted by a point source varies as the inverse square of the distance from that source.

The flux density (F) of radiation from a surface at a distance (D) is the amount of radiant energy passing through an area perpendicular to the line of sight of the emitting surface. Mathematically, this may be written as

$$F = \frac{W\,A}{\pi\,D^2} \qquad (2\text{-}12)$$

or by substitution from Equation 2-5,

$$F = \frac{\epsilon \sigma T^4\,A}{\pi D^2} \qquad (2\text{-}13)$$

or by substitution with Equation 2-10,

$$F = I\,\frac{A}{D^2} \qquad (2\text{-}14)$$

where,
    F equals flux density,
    A equals area of emitting surface,
    D equals distance from emitting surface to receiving surface.

Example—Assume a surface of 2 centimeters by 2 centimeters to be emitting 100 watts of radiant energy. What would the flux density be at a distance of 10 meters?

Answer—Using Equation 2-12,

$$F = \frac{100 \text{ W} \times 2 \text{ cm} \times 2 \text{ cm}}{\text{cm}^2 \ \pi \ 100 \text{ cm}^2}$$

$$= \frac{400 \text{ W cm}^2}{\text{cm}^2 \ 314 \text{ cm}^2} = \frac{1.27 \text{ W}}{\text{cm}^2}$$

Radiant energy, in its interaction with matter, behaves as though it consists of bundles of energy called *photons*. The amount of energy in each photon is equal to its frequency times Planck's quantum constant, or

$$\xi = hf \tag{2-15}$$

where,

ξ equals photon energy in joules,
h equals Planck's quantum constant $(6.62 \times 10^{-34} \text{ W s}^2)$,
f equals frequency in hertz.

Example—What is the energy of each photon emitted at a wavelength of 1 micrometer?

Answer—From Equation 1-1,

$$f = \frac{c}{\lambda} = \frac{3 \times 10^8}{1 \times 10^{-6}} = 3 \times 10^{14} \text{ Hz}$$

$$\xi = 6.62 \times 10^{-34} \text{ W s}^2 \times 3 \times 10^{14} \text{ Hz}$$

$$= 19.86 \times 10^{-20} \text{ J}$$

Equations 2-5, 2-7, and 2-8 may also be expressed in terms of photon flux. The photon distribution is given by

$$Q_\lambda = \frac{\epsilon_\lambda \ c_1}{\lambda^4 \ (e^{c2/\lambda T} - 1)} \tag{2-16}$$

where,

Q_λ is the photon flux emitted by an object at a given wavelength (λ), and all other symbols are the same as those used in Equation 2-8.

When the function Q_λ is integrated over the total spectral region from zero to infinity, the total number of emitted photons becomes

$$Q = \epsilon T^3 \frac{1.52 \times 10^{11} \text{ photons}}{\text{s cm}^2} \tag{2-17}$$

where Q is the total number of emitted photons per second.

Example—How many photons are emitted from a 500-kelvin blackbody?

Answer—From Equation 2-17,

$$Q = \frac{1 \, [1.52 \times 10^{11} \times (5 \times 10^2)^3]}{\text{s cm}^2}$$

$$= \frac{1.9 \times 10^{19} \text{ photons}}{\text{s cm}^2}$$

The photon distribution is shifted toward longer wavelengths and the peak may be determined by the following equation:

$$\lambda_{max} = \frac{3.67 \times 10^3 \, \mu\text{m K}}{T} \qquad (2\text{-}18)$$

Example—At what wavelength will the maximum amount of photons be emitted from a 1223-kelvin source?

Answer—From Equation 2-18,

$$\lambda_{max} = \frac{3.67 \times 10^3 \, \mu\text{m K}}{1.223 \times 10^3} = 3 \, \mu\text{m}$$

INFRARED SOURCES

As mentioned previously, all objects emit infrared radiation. Therefore, all objects are sources of infrared energy.

Infrared sources may be classified in two general areas: natural and artificial.

Natural sources include celestial objects such as the sun, stars, and planets; terrestrial objects such as plants, rocks, minerals, and the sea; and man-made sources such as ovens, engines, molten metals, light bulbs, and even the human body.

Artificial Sources

We first consider the blackbody.

Blackbody Radiators—A blackbody, by definition, is a perfect radiator of infrared energy. Since there are no perfect radiators found in nature a blackbody is an artificial source. That is, it must be constructed.

According to Kirchhoff's law (Equation 2-2), a perfect emitter is also a perfect absorber. If we can prove that an object is a perfect absorber (it will absorb all of the energy incident upon it), then we can be satisfied that it will also be a perfect emitter.

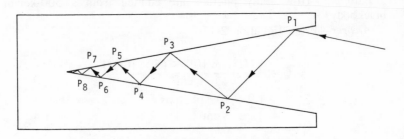

Fig. 2-8. Radiation reflection within conical cavity.

Fig. 2-8 shows the cross section of a material having a conical cavity. If a beam of infrared radiation were aimed into the conical cavity, it would be reflected many times within the cavity before it could be reflected back out. Let's look at what happens to this beam of infrared energy.

First, let's make three assumptions. One is that the material is opaque and has an emissivity value of 0.5 (therefore, a reflectivity of 0.5). The second assumption is that the angle of the cavity is such that the incoming beam will be reflected ten times before it exits. Then, let's assume that the incoming beam is 100 watts of infrared energy.

As the 100 watts of infrared energy strikes point P_1, 50 watts will be absorbed and 50 watts will be reflected.

At P_2, 50 percent of the impinging 50 watts (or 25 watts) will be absorbed and 50 percent will be reflected. At this time 75 percent of the incident radiation has been absorbed (50 percent at P_1 and 25 percent at P_2) and 25 percent is being reflected to P_3.

An additional 12.5 watts will be absorbed at P_3. Also 6.25 watts will be absorbed at P_4, 3.125 watts at P_5, 1.5625 watts at P_6, 0.781 watt at P_7, 0.391 at P_8, 0.195 at P_9, and 0.0976 at P_{10}. At this time over 99.9 watts of energy have been absorbed into the cavity. Only 0.0976 watt is allowed to be reflected back out.

Typical values for the angle of conical cavities available from commercial sources are 12 degrees to 15 degrees.

Emissivity may be increased if the emissivity of the cavity walls is increased, or if the number of internal reflections is increased. (See Table 2-4.) For practical purposes a cavity is considered black if it has an emissivity value greater than 0.98. In no instance can the emissivity value of an object exceed 1.0.

Various types of common blackbody cavity configurations are shown in Fig. 2-9. The spherical cavity is generally considered best for blackbodies but not as practical as the conical or cylindrical cavities.

Table 2-4. Effective Emissivity Values

Number of Reflections	Emissivity of Material				
	0.2	0.4	0.6	0.8	1.0
1	0.20	0.40	0.60	0.80	1.0
2	0.36	0.64	0.84	0.96	1.0
3	0.49	0.78	0.94	0.99	1.0
4	0.59	0.87	0.96	0.99	1.0
5	0.67	0.92	0.98	0.99	1.0
6	0.73	0.95	0.99	0.99	1.0
7	0.79	0.97	0.99	0.99	1.0
8	0.83	0.98	0.99	0.99	1.0
9	0.86	0.99	0.99	0.99	1.0
10	0.88	0.99	0.99	0.99	1.0

A blackbody may be visualized as a large enclosure having a small opening. One may visualize a blackbody enclosure by thinking of an average size room (the enclosure) with a window (the small opening). At noon, the room will be well lighted from the visible radiation entering the window.

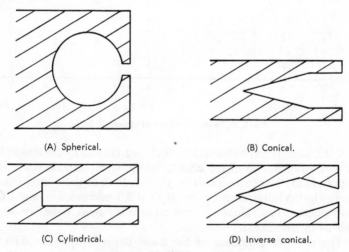

(A) Spherical.   (B) Conical.

(C) Cylindrical.   (D) Inverse conical.

Fig. 2-9. Blackbody cavities.

To an observer on the outside, however, the room will appear to be "black." All of the visible radiation is entering the window but little or no visible radiation is leaving. Thus, a blackbody condition exists.

Any hole in any material increases the effective emissivity value of that material. In general, if a hole is at least five times deeper than its opening, it may be considered to be a blackbody. Fig. 2-10 shows the effective emissivity values for a number of hole depths: hole size ratios and various actual emissivity values. The curves are for a cylindrical hole, where d is the depth of the hole, r is the radius of the hole, and ϵ the emissivity of the material containing the hole.

Nonblackbody Radiators—There are many nonblackbody types of infrared sources used in industry and research laboratories. Among those sources commonly used are flames, tungsten lamps, Nernst glowers, and lasers.

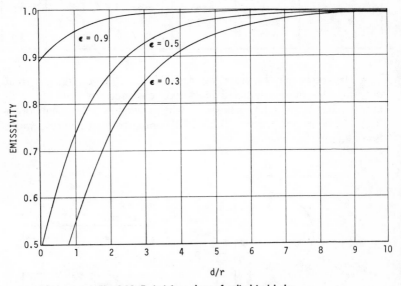

Fig. 2-10. Emissivity values of cylindrical holes.

Flames: When hydrocarbon fuels are burned in the atmosphere, or with oxygen, two of the combustion products produced are water vapor (H_2O) and carbon dioxide (CO_2). Both of these products emit energy in the infrared spectrum: H_2O at 2.7 micrometers, and CO_2 at 4.45 micrometers. There are numerous other weak bands between 1 and 24 micrometers.

The effective emittance of the flame depends upon its thickness, temperature, and pressure at which the exhaust gases escape. Fig. 2-11 shows the emission characteristics of a natural gas flame. Other flame emissions may vary slightly but the strong emission at 2.7 and 4.45 micrometers will always be apparent.

Tungsten Lamps: Tungsten filaments are excellent sources of relatively high energies of infrared radiation.

At 2500 kelvins a tungsten filament has an emissivity of about 0.31 and emits about 68 watts per square centimeter per second.

When placed within a glass envelope the energy emitted from the tungstent filament is reduced by the transmissivity of the glass. Since glass does not normally transmit wavelengths longer than 3 micrometers, a tungsten lamp is only useful as a source of near infrared, or visible, radiation.

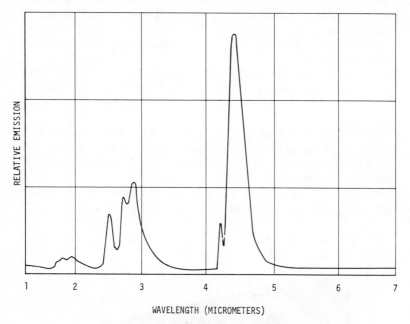

WAVELENGTH (MICROMETERS)

Fig. 2-11. Emission of natural gas flame.

Nernst glower: A Nernst glower is a cylindrical rod of refractory oxides. It is essentially a graybody with peak spectral emittance occuring at about two micrometers (about 1200°C). The Nernst glower is commonly used as a standard source for spectrophotometers and other similar laboratory instruments.

Laser: A laser is a source of coherent radiation (monochromatic). Lasers emit energy at specific wavelengths. The wavelength at which a laser emits is dependent upon the active medium used by the laser.

A carbon-dioxide (CO_2) laser emits energy at 10.6 micrometers. Ten-watt CO_2 lasers are readily available. Some CO_2 lasers emit more than 1000 watts at 10.6 micrometers. Fig. 2-12 shows a CO_2 laser.

Another common infrared laser is the neodymium doped yttrium aluminum garnet (Nd:YAG). The Nd:YAG lasers emit about 10

31

watts of energy at 1.06 micrometers. Most other lasers emit visible radiation.

Natural Sources

Natural sources include the sun, the sea, plants, and even the human body.

Sun—The sun approximates a blackbody at a temperature of about 5500° Celsius. Over 50 percent of the solar radiation is in the infrared portion of the electromagnetic spectrum. The sun's peak energy is emitted at about 0.5 micrometer.

Distant stars are similar sources of infrared energy differing only in size and temperature.

Sea—Water has essentially zero transmission at infrared wavelengths and therefore approximates a blackbody condition. Standard blackbody spectral and total emittances can be assumed for fresh and salt water.

Plants—Plants and soils may be considered graybody sources. Most plants and almost all soils have emissivity values of greater than 0.93. The moisture content of soil or plants has little, if any, effect on their emissivity characteristics.

Human Body—Human skin at a normal temperature of 37° Celsius emits more than 50 percent of its radiant energy between 5 and 14 micrometers. The peak energy is emitted at 9.3 micrometers.

The infrared emittance of human skin, regardless of visible color, very closely approaches unity (emissivity equal to 1.0).

Courtesy Sylvania Electric Products, Inc.

Fig. 2-12. Carbon-dioxide laser.

ATMOSPHERIC ABSORPTION

The transmission of infrared radiation through the atmosphere is effected by the absorption characteristics of the many constituents found in the atmosphere.

The atmosphere is composed of gases, liquids, and solid particles, all of which attenuate or scatter infrared radiation in one way or an-

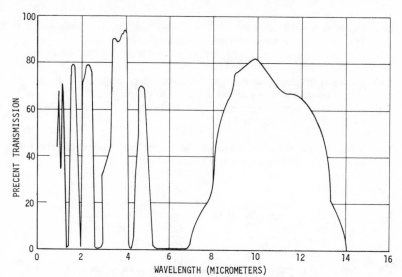

Fig. 2-13. Water vapor transmission characteristics.

other. About 78 percent of the air we breathe is nitrogen and 20 percent is oxygen; the rest consists of helium, argon, carbon dioxide, hydrogen, methane, neon, krypton, and ozone.

Water vapor (H_2O) is probably the single most important attenuator of infrared radiation. Major water vapor bands occur at 1.38, 1.87, 2.7, and 6.3 micrometers (Fig. 2-13). Most water vapor is near the surface of the earth.

Carbon dioxide (CO_2) and ozone (O_2) are two other major contributors to the attenuation of passing infrared energy. Carbon dioxide absorbs strongest at 2.0, 2.7, 4.3, and 15.0 micrometers. Ozone bands absorb energy between 9.3 and 9.8 micrometers.

Infrared instruments and systems should avoid all or most of the atmospheric absorption bands, where practical, for maximum signal conditions. Calibration of infrared systems does vary with atmospheric path length and humidity.

QUESTIONS

2-1. What is the relationship between absorptivity (α), reflectivity (ρ) and transmissivity (τ)?

A. $\alpha = \rho + \tau$.   C. $1 = \alpha - (\rho + \tau)$.
B. $1 = \alpha + \rho + \tau$.   D. $\alpha + \rho = 1 + \tau$.

2-2. What is the correct relationship between emissivity (ϵ) and absorptivity (α)?

A. $1 = \epsilon + \alpha$.   C. $\epsilon = \alpha$.
B. $\epsilon = 1 - \alpha$.   D. $\epsilon = 1 + \alpha$.

2-3. Emisivity may be stated as:
   A. The difference between absorptivity and reflectivity.
   B. The ratio between energy emitted by a blackbody and the reflectivity of the blackbody.
   C. The ratio of energy emitted by an object at a temperature T and the energy emitted by a blackbody at the same temperature T.
   D. The total radiant energy emitted by a blackbody divided by the transmissivity of that blackbody.

2-4. Which of the following equations is correct for determining the total amount of radiant energy emitted by an object?
   A. $W = \epsilon\sigma T$.
   B. $W = 2\epsilon\sigma T^4$.
   C. $W = \epsilon T^4$.
   D. $W = \epsilon\sigma T^4$.

2-5. What is the correct value of the Stefan-Boltzman constant?
   A. 5.67×10^{-5} W/cm.
   B. 5.67×10^{-12} W/cm^2 K^4.
   C. 5.67×10^{12} W/cm^2.
   D. 5.67 W/K^4.

2-6. Wien's displacement law for determining the peak wavelength of emitted radiation may be expressed as:
   A. $\lambda = \dfrac{2.89 \times 10^3 \ \mu m \ K}{T}$.
   B. $\lambda = 2.89 \times 10^3 T$.
   C. $\lambda = \dfrac{K}{2.89 \times 10^3 \ \mu m}$.
   D. $\lambda = 2.89 \times 10^3 \ (\epsilon\sigma T)^4$.

2-7. Lambert's law states that:
   A. The energy emitted from a surface is constant from any angle of emission.
   B. The amount of energy emitted from a surface varies as the cosine of the angle from which it leaves that surface.
   C. The amount of energy emitted from a surface varies as sine of the angle from which it leaves that surface.
   D. The amount of energy emitted from a surface varies as the square of the cosine of the angle from which it leaves that surface.

2-8. What is the correct formula for determining photon energy?
   A. $\xi = fc$.
   B. $\xi = hf$.
   C. $\xi = hc$.
   D. $\xi = h\tau$.

3

OPTICS

All infrared systems require a transmitter and a receiver. Optics may be used at the transmitter to shape, direct, or modify the infrared radiation before it reaches the receiver. The receiver may use optical techniques to help collect and focus the incoming radiation onto an infrared detector.

To better understand the fundamentals of optical systems, this chapter will first discuss geometrical optics and then physical optics.

GEOMETRICAL OPTICS

Geometrical optics considers infrared radiation to be continuous linear rays of energy. This treatment of radiation as straight, narrow beams has been used for many years to explain the basic principles of optics.

We learned in Chapter 2, however, that infrared radiation consists of "bundles of energy" called photons. The section on physical optics will deal with radiation as photons or particles of light. This approach is needed to explain some of the phenomenon associated with optics that cannot be explained by the geometrical consideration.

Reflection

Almost all surfaces reflect some percentage of infrared radiation. Mirrors and shiny metal surfaces are usually good reflectors. Carbon, cloth, and paper are generally poor reflectors of infrared radiation.

There are two fundamental laws of reflection. They are: (1) the incident ray, the normal, and the reflected ray are in the same plane, and (2) the angle of incidence is equal to the angle of reflection. Refering to Fig. 3-1, the second law of reflection may be written as

$$\theta_i = \theta_r \qquad \text{(3-1)}$$

where,

θ_i equals angle of incidence,
θ_r equals angle of reflection.

The two laws of reflection apply to specular reflection such as occurs when rays are reflected from a mirror. In this instance the reflected beam has almost all the same characteristics as the incident beam.

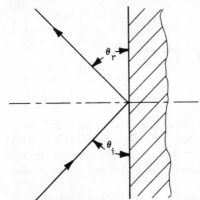

Fig. 3-1. The second law of reflection.

Another type of reflection is called *diffused reflection*. Diffused reflection occurs when the incident beam is reflected in many directions such as happens when a flashlight is pointed at a sheet of paper. The light can be seen at any angle and is called diffused light.

If the flashlight were aimed at a mirror, the specularly reflected light could only be seen by viewing from the angle of reflection.

Refraction

We learned in Chapter 1 that infrared radiation travels through space at the speed of light. Radiation traveling through other mediums, such as glass, travels at a lower velocity.

When a beam of infrared radiation travels from one medium to another its direction is altered and the beam appears to bend. This "bending" of the beam is called *refraction* and is due to the change in beam velocity.

Infrared rays entering a more dense medium (such as air to glass) will bend toward the normal of the incident surface. (See Fig. 3-2.) When that beam passes from glass to air (into a less dense medium) the beam will bend away from the normal.

There are two common laws of refraction. The first law states that the incident ray, the normal, and the refracted ray are in the same plane.

The second law is often referred to as *Snell's law*. It states that for monochromatic light (of a single wavelength), the ratio of the sine of the angle of incidence to the sine of the angle of refraction is a constant. Mathematically,

$$\frac{\sin \theta_i}{\sin \theta_r} = n_r \qquad (3\text{-}2)$$

where,

θ_i equals angle of incidence,
θ_r equals angle of refraction,
n_r equals relative index of refraction.

Example—What is the relative index of refraction for a material that refracts an incident beam at 20 degrees to the normal to 15 degrees?

Answer—From Equation 3-2,

$$n_r = \frac{\sin 20°}{\sin 15°} = \frac{0.342}{0.258} = 1.32$$

The *absolute* index of refraction is determined when an infrared ray passes from a vacuum into a medium. This may be written as

$$n = \frac{c}{v}$$

where,

n equals absolute index of refraction,
c equals velocity of light in vacuum (3×10^8 m/s),
v equals velocity of light in medium.

When a beam of radiation passes through a transparent medium (with parallel surfaces) the beam is displaced parallel to itself, as can be seen in Fig. 3-2.

The angle of refraction into a less dense medium in some instances may be parallel to the surface of the medium. This angle is called the *critical angle* and is shown in Fig. 3-3. Note that if the angle of incidence is greater than the critical angle, the beam will not enter the new medium but will be reflected back into the original medium.

Dispersion—We have seen that the index of refraction varies with the velocity of a monochromatic beam as it passes through a medium. The index of refraction also varies with wavelength. A medium in which the velocity of a beam depends upon the wavelength is called a *dispersive medium*. It is this characteristic, of some mediums, that disperses white light into the colors of the spectrum, as shown in Fig. 3-4. Note that shorter wavelengths, such as blue or ultraviolet, are refracted more than longer wavelengths, such as red or infrared.

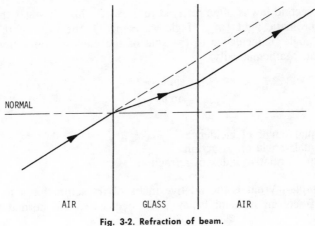
Fig. 3-2. Refraction of beam.

Mirrors—Fig. 3-5 shows the basic quantities needed to examine how an image is formed from a spherical mirror. For a collimated (parallel) beam of light, the focal length of a concave spherical mirror is given as

$$f = \frac{R}{2} \tag{3-4}$$

where,
    f equals focal length,
    R equals radius of curvature of the mirror.

Example—What is the focal length of a spherical mirror with a radius of 12 inches?

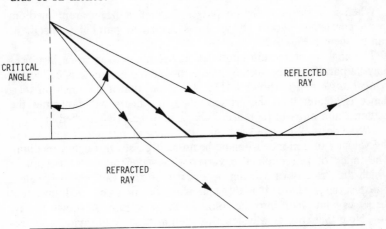
Fig. 3-3. Illustrating the critical angle.

Answer—From Equation 3-4,

$$f = \frac{12}{2} = 6 \text{ inches}$$

The relation between object distance (d), image distance (d') and radius of curvature (R) may be written as

$$\frac{1}{d} + \frac{1}{d'} = \frac{2}{R} \qquad (3\text{-}5)$$

where,

d equals object distance (from object to surface of mirror),
d' equals image distance (from image to surface of mirror),
R equals radius of curvature of the mirror.

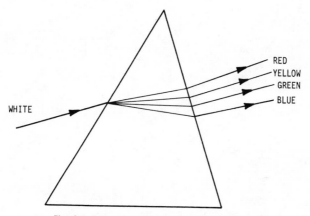

Fig. 3-4. Dispersion of white light by a prism.

By substituting Equations 3-4 and 3-5 we find that

$$\frac{1}{d'} = \frac{1}{f} - \frac{1}{d} \qquad (3\text{-}6)$$

Example—An object is 60 inches from the spherical mirror with a focal length of 6 inches. How far from the surface of the mirror will that object's image appear?

Answer—From Equation 3-6,

$$\frac{1}{d'} = \frac{1}{f} - \frac{1}{d} = \frac{1}{6} - \frac{1}{60} = \frac{3}{20}$$

Thus

$$d' = 6.66 \text{ inches}$$

The *magnification* of an optical system may be defined as

$$m = \frac{y'}{y} \qquad (3\text{-}7)$$

where,

    m equals magnification,
    y' equals image size,
    y equals object size.

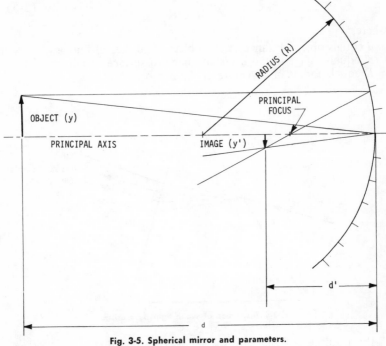

Fig. 3-5. Spherical mirror and parameters.

Example—What is the magnification of an optical system that produces an image of 0.25 inches from an object of 5 inches?

Answer—From Equation 3-7,

$$m = \frac{y'}{y} = \frac{0.25}{5} = 0.05$$

When the magnification is less than 1.0 it means that the image is smaller than the object. No attempt has been made in this chapter to distinguish real or virtual images or to determine whether an image is erect or inverted.

Lenses—Lenses of transparent materials are used to form images. Lenses may be used singly or in combination with other lenses or mirrors.

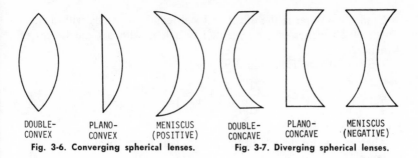

| DOUBLE-
CONVEX | PLANO-
CONVEX | MENISCUS
(POSITIVE) | DOUBLE-
CONCAVE | PLANO-
CONCAVE | MENISCUS
(NEGATIVE) |

Fig. 3-6. Converging spherical lenses.   **Fig. 3-7. Diverging spherical lenses.**

Spherical lenses are most popular because they are easiest to make. A spherical lens may be converging or diverging.

Converging lenses are thicker at the center than at the edges (Fig. 3-6). Diverging lenses are thinner at the center than at the edges (Fig. 3-7).

The characteristics of a lens are due to the refraction of light as it enters and leaves the lens surfaces.

The following formula applies for a thin lens, as shown in Fig. 3-8:

$$\frac{1}{d} + \frac{1}{d'} = \frac{1}{f} \tag{3-8}$$

where,

d equals object distance,
d' equals image distance,
f equals focal length of the lens.

Equation 3-8 is called the lensmaker's equation. Note that Equation 3-8 is the same as Equation 3-6. The magnification of a lens may also be expressed as in Equation 3-7.

If two lenses are placed in contact so that their principal axes coincide, they may be considered as one lens with a focal point of

$$\frac{1}{f} = \frac{1}{f_1} + \frac{1}{f_2} \tag{3-9}$$

where,

f equals effective focal length,
f_1 equals focal length of first lens,
f_2 equals focal length of second lens.

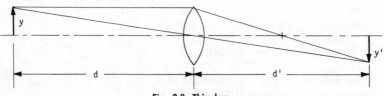

Fig. 3-8. Thin lens.

Example—What is the effective focal length of a lens with a focal length of 20 inches when cemented to a lens with a focal length of 4 inches?

Answer—From Equation 3-9,

$$\frac{1}{f} = \frac{1}{20} + \frac{1}{4} = \frac{3}{10}$$

So $f = 3.33$ inches.

Aberrations are defects in the images which are formed by mirrors or lenses.

Spherical Aberrations—When a beam of parallel rays is focused by a large spherical mirror or lens, all of the reflected or refracted rays do not pass through the principal focus. In effect, there is no sharp focal point.

Parabolic mirrors may be used in place of spherical mirrors to eliminate spherical aberrations. In the case of lenses, a diaphragm may be used to limit the rays to the central portion of lens to reduce spherical abberations.

Chromatic Aberrations—As discussed previously, the focal length of a lens depends upon its index of refraction. Most lens materials are dispersive; that is, they have different indices of refraction for different wavelengths.

When a ray of light consisting of many wavelengths passes through a lens, the focal point for the shorter wavelength will be closer to the lens (Fig. 3-9). The differences in focal length due to the refractive index of the lens is called *chromatic aberration.*

Achromatic (meaning free of color) lenses are used to correct for distortion due to chromatic aberration. Achromatic lenses are made by combining elements of different kinds of glass. Reflective optical systems (those that use mirrors) do not produce chromatic aberrations.

f Number—The f number of a lens is an indication of the lenses' capacity for collecting incoming radiation. The f number (or focal ratio) is the ratio of the lens focal length to the effective diameter of the lens, or, mathematically,

$$f\# = \frac{f}{d} \tag{3-10}$$

where,
 f# equals f number,
 f equals focal length of lens,
 d equals effective lens diameter.

Example—What is the f number of a lens with a focal length of 6 inches and a diameter of 2 inches?

Answer—From Equation 3-10,

$$f\# = \frac{6}{2} = 3$$

An f1 lens is considered faster than an f3 lens. The faster the lens, the more radiation it will collect. For imaging systems a low f number is preferred; however, low f-number optical systems have large entrance diameters and are more subject to aberrations and sharper depths of focus.

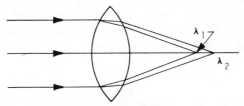

Fig. 3-9. Illustrating chromatic aberration, with $\lambda_1 < \lambda_2$.

PHYSICAL OPTICS

The previous pages have dealt with light as though it traveled in straight lines (geometrical optics). This theoretical approach is fine for understanding many of the basic optical principles.

We noted earlier, however, that light and infrared radiation is actually electromagnetic radiation and travels in bundles of energy called photons. To better understand the phenomenon of interference, diffraction, polarization, and scattering, it is necessary to discuss what is commonly referred to as physical optics.

Interference

Light which is striking a thin transparent material is partially reflected by the first surface, partially reflected by the second surface, and partially transmitted through the material as shown in Fig. 3-10.

Depending on the thickness of the transparent material, the light reflected from the second surface may be in phase or out of phase with the light reflected from the first surface.

If the reflections are in phase, they will tend to reinforce each other; if opposite in phase, they will tend to cancel each other. The result will appear as a series of light and dark stripes if the light is monochromatic or as a series of different color stripes if the light is incoherent (of many wavelengths).

We observe this phenomena when we see bright color patterns on soap bubbles or oil films. Interference is observed only when the thickness of the film is close to an integral or half-integral multiple of the wavelength of light.

The interference produced by thin films may be used to reduce the loss of radiant energy by reflection which normally takes place at the surface of lenses or windows in optical systems. Interference filters may also be produced to reflect many wavelengths and transmit only a desired wavelength or wavelengths.

Diffraction

Diffraction, or a certain "blending" of rays, is caused when light passes a sharp opaque edge. A beam of collimated light passing through a narrow slit will produce a pattern consisting of a bright image of the slit and a series of bright and dark fringes on both sides of central image. The intensity of the fringes will decrease as the distance from the central image is increased.

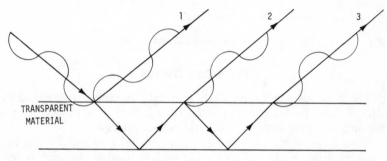

Fig. 3-10. Reflection and transmission of light from and in a thin transparent medium.

An optical system having a very small aperture will produce a diffraction pattern consisting of a bright central disc surrounded by fainter circular rings.

The resolving power of lens is limited by the diffraction phenomena. The size of the diffraction pattern is determined by the wavelength, effective diameter, and focal length of the lens used.

The best image that can be formed by an optical system may be determined by the following formula:

$$\theta = 1.22\frac{\lambda}{d} \tag{3-11}$$

where,
    θ equals angle of resolution in radians,
    λ equals wavelength,
    d equals diameter of aperture.

Example—What is the best angle of resolution obtainable from an optical system for a wavelength of 1 μm with a 5-mm aperture?

Answer—From Equation 3-11,

$$\theta = 1.22 \frac{\lambda}{d} = 1.22 \frac{10^{-6}}{5 \times 10^{-3}}$$

$$= 0.244 \text{ milliradian}$$

Polarization

Infrared waves are called *transverse waves;* that is, they oscillate at right angles to the direction in which they travel.

Unpolarized waves oscillate in all directions perpendicular to the direction of the wave. *Polarized waves* consist of wave trains that oscillate in only one direction perpendicular to the direction of the wave.

Infrared waves may be completely polarized, partially polarized, or unpolarized. Polarization occurs naturally by reflection or scattering. Fig. 3-11 shows an unpolarized beam striking a transparent material. The reflected beam is horizontally polarized. If the impinging radiation were horizontally polarized then all of the energy would be reflected.

Reflected unpolarized radiation from nonmetallic surfaces is generally partially polarized. If the tangent of the angle of reflection is equal to the index of refraction of the reflecting medium, then the reflected energy will be completely plane polarized. This angle is referred to as *Brewster's angle* and may be written as

$$\tan \theta_r = n \qquad (3-12)$$

where,

θ_r equals angle of reflection,
n equals index of refraction.

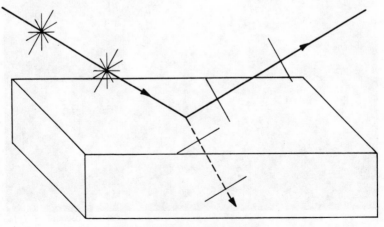

Fig. 3-11. Polarization by reflection.

Example—What is the Brewster angle for germanium, which has an index of refraction of 4.0?

Answer—From Equation 3-12,

$$\tan \theta_r = 4.0$$

The Brewster angle is thus 76 degrees.

MATERIALS

There are three basic uses for optical materials. They are windows, refractive components such as lenses, and substrates.

Optical materials may be classified into glasses and crystals. Some typical glasses are those of oxide, aluminate, gallate, tellurite, and selenide. Crystals may be of various fluorides and some semiconductors such as germanium. In general, glasses are less expensive and available in larger sizse.

Many materials are available for use with infrared systems. Only the most common ones will be described.

Properties

Optical components must normally withstand severe environmental conditions. It is therefore important to choose materials having durability, strength, and thermal and mechanical shock resistance in addition to their optical properties. Fig. 3-12 shows some common optical materials.

Courtesy OCLI, Inc.

Fig. 3-12. Optical materials.

Table 3-1. Material Properties

Material	Symbol	Melting or Softening Temperature (°C)	Solubility (g/100 g water)	Coefficient of Thermal Expansion (10^{-6}/°C)	Hardness (Knoop number)
Ammonium Dihydrogen Phosphate	ADP	–	22.7	–	–
Arsenic Trisulfide	As_2S_3	210	*	25	109
Calcide	$CaCO_3$	895	0.0014	25	–
Calcium Fluoride	CaF_2	1360	0.0017	24	158
Cesium Iodide	CsI	620	44.0	50	–
Crystal Quartz	SiO_2	1460	*	8	741
Fused Silica	SiO_2	1700	*	0.5	461
Germanium	Ge	935	*	6	–
Indium Arsenide	InAs	942	*	5	–
Lithium Fluoride	LiF	870	0.27	37	110
Magnesium Oxide	MgO	2800	*	14	692
Potassium Bromide	KBr	730	53.5	43	6
Potassium Chloride	KCl	775	34.7	36	8
Potassium Dihydrogen Phosphate	KDP	252	33.0	–	1370
Sapphire	Al_2O_3	2030	*	6	–
Silicon	Si	1420	*	4	1150
Sodium Chloride	NaCl	820	35.7	44	16
Sodium Fluoride	NAF	980	4.22	36	–
Thallium Bromide-Iodide	KRS-5	415	0.05	58	40

*Insoluble.

Some of the more important properties of optical materials are as follows:

Transmission—The percent of transmission relative to wavelength and thickness is an important consideration when choosing optical materials.

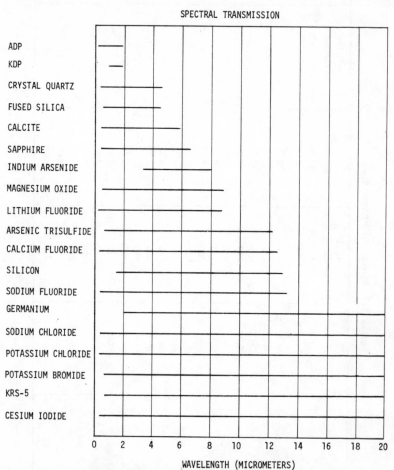

SPECTRAL TRANSMISSION

Fig. 3-13. Transmission spectra of common materials.

Index of Refraction—This must be known for design of lenses and polarizing elements. Also needed to compute losses due to reflection.

Hardness—The hardness of an optical material should be chosen so as to offer minium distortion due to stress.

Solubility—The ability to dissolve in water. Optical materials should be resistant to ambient atmospheric conditions.

Thermal Expansion—This should be chosen to match the mounting materials to prevent cracking or stress.

Melting Temperature—Consideration should be given to the melting or softening temperature of all optical materials.

Thermal Conductivity—This is how fast the material will heat or cool. Temperature variations in most optical materials cause changes in refractive index and transmission.

Some common materials and their properties are shown in Table 3-1 and Figs. 3-13 and 3-14.

Fiber Optics

Some smooth transparent rods transmit visible and infrared energy by multiple internal reflections. This phenomenon is called *total internal reflection*. Transmission of light can also take place in a very small diameter rod such as a fiber.

A portion of the light entering a fiber will emerge from the opposite end. The loss in transmission is due to the absorption of the transmitting media, scattering, and end-surface reflection.

The transmission of a fiber is increased by coating a high-refractive-index core with a substance of low refractive index.

The light-gathering power of an optical fiber is known as the *numerical aperture* and may be defined as

$$NA = \sqrt{n_1{}^2 - n_2{}^2} \qquad (3\text{-}13)$$

where,

NA equals numerical aperture,
n_1 equals refractive index of fiber,
n_2 equals refractive index of coating.

Example—What is the numerical aperture of a glass fiber with a refractive index of 2.3 and coated with a material having a refractive index of 1.4?

Answer—From Equation 3-13,

$$NA = \sqrt{(2.3)^2 - (1.4)^2} = \sqrt{3.33}$$
$$= 1.82$$

Filters

Many infrared systems require selection of certain wavelengths. Spectral filtering techniques can be used to observe specific wavelength regions or reduce background radiation.

The most common types of spectral filters are the absorption filter and the interference filter. The absorption filter combines the natural transmission characteristics of two or more optical materials. Fig. 3-15 shows the transmission spectrum obtained by combining sapphire and indium arsenide.

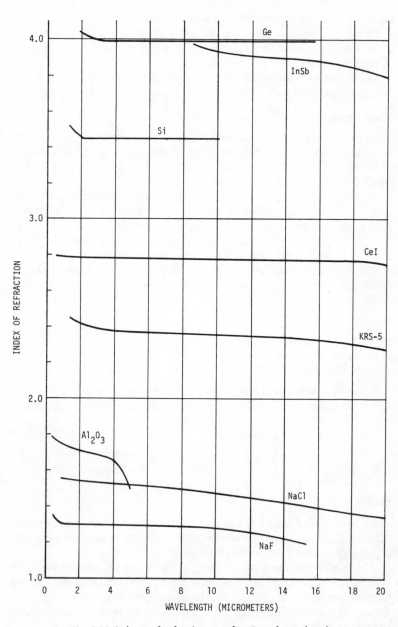

Fig. 3-14. Indexes of refraction as a function of wavelength.

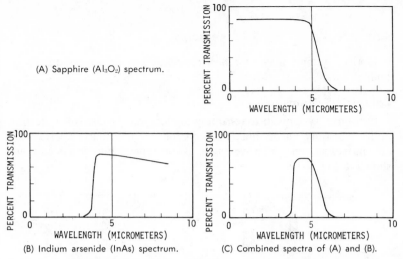

(A) Sapphire (Al₃O₂) spectrum.

(B) Indium arsenide (InAs) spectrum.

(C) Combined spectra of (A) and (B).

Fig. 3-15. Transmission spectrum of combined materials.

The interference filter is made of multiple layers of dielectric materials of alternately high and low refractive indices. Accurate control of the substrate material, absorption characteristics of the coatings, and number of layers can provide filters for almost any desired spectral response.

Spectral filters may be long-pass, short-pass, or band-pass as shown in Fig. 3-16. Narrow–band-pass filters are sometimes called *spike filters*.

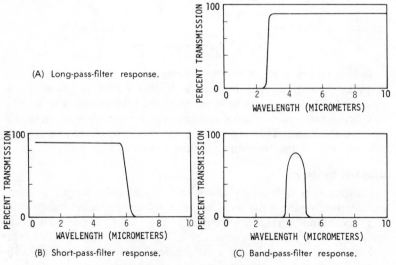

(A) Long-pass-filter response.

(B) Short-pass-filter response.

(C) Band-pass-filter response.

Fig. 3-16. Responses of spectral filters.

SYSTEMS

Optical systems may be reflective, refractive, or a combination of both.

Catoptric Systems

Catoptric systems use reflecting optics solely. Use of reflecting optics generally means high transmission, no chromatic aberrations, and no restrictions on wavelength. Some typical mirror systems are shown in Fig. 3-17.

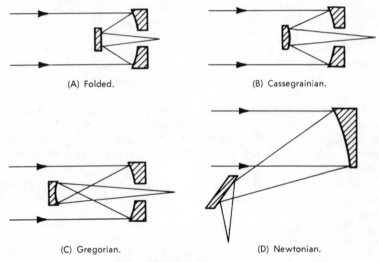

(A) Folded.　　　　　　　　　　(B) Cassegrainian.

(C) Gregorian.　　　　　　　　(D) Newtonian.

Fig. 3-17. Typical mirror systems.

Folded mirror systems are most common in infrared radiometers. A folded system using a hyperbolic folding mirror is known as a *Cassegrainian system*: one using a parabolic folding mirror is known as a *Gregorian system*. Folded systems introduce an obstruction to the enter of the beam. This can be eliminated by use of off-axis optical systems such as the Newtonian system shown in Fig. 3-17.

Dioptric Systems

Dioptric systems use only lenses and may be quite simple or complex, depending upon the focal length, resolution, spectral bandwidth, and aberration corrections required. Fig. 3-18 shows two such systems.

Representative simple lens configurations were shown in Figs. 3-6 and 3-7.

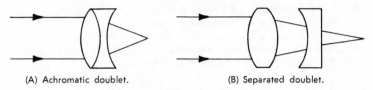

(A) Achromatic doublet.　　　　(B) Separated doublet.

Fig. 3-18. Dioptric systems.

Catadioptric Systems

Systems combining reflective and refractive optics are known as *catadioptric systems*. Some such systems are shown in Fig. 3-19.

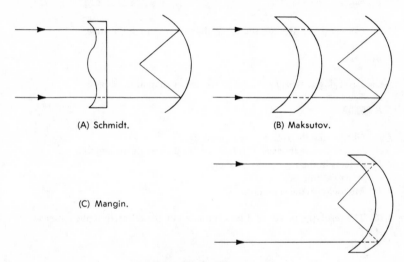

(A) Schmidt.　　　　(B) Maksutov.

(C) Mangin.

Fig. 3-19. Catadioptric systems.

QUESTIONS

3-1. The second law of reflection may be stated as:
  A. The angle of incidence is equal to one-half the angle of reflection.
  B. The angle of reflection is equal to one-half the angle of incidence.
  C. The angle of incidence is equal to the angle of reflection.
  D. The angle of reflection is equal to the angle of refraction.

3-2. Refraction is caused by:
  A. A change in wavelength.
  B. A change in beam velocity.
  C. A change in reflection.
  D. A change in frequency.

3-3. Snell's law may be written as:
  A. $\sin \theta_i = \sin \theta_r$.
  B. $n_r = \sin \theta_i / \sin \theta_r$.
  C. $\sin \theta_i = n_r$.
  D. $\theta_i = \theta_r$.

3-4. A dispersive medium is a medium in which:
A. The velocity of a beam depends on wavelength.
B. The velocity of a beam depends on the refractive index.
C. The refractive index is less than that of air.
D. The refractive index is greater than that of air.

3-5. The focal length of a concave mirror is:
A. $f = 2R/d$.   C. $f = 2d$.
B. $f = R/d$.   D. $f = R/2$.

3-6. The relationship between object distance, image distance, and focal length is:
A. $f = d + d'$.   C. $1/f = 1/d + 1/d'$.
B. $f = d - d'$.   D. $1/f = 1/d - 1/d'$.

3-7. Converging lenses are thicker at the center than at the edges.
A. True.
B. False.

3-8. Diverging lenses are thicker at the center than at the edges.
A. True.
B. False.

3-9. Chromatic aberrations are caused by:
A. Differences in indexes of refraction for different wavelengths.
B. Defects in the roundness of a lens.
C. Spherical mirrors.
D. Monochromatic radiation.

3-10. The resolving power of a lens is limited by the diffraction phenomena.
A. True.
B. False.

3-11. Brewster's angle may be written as:
A. $\sin \theta_r = n$.   C. $\cos \theta_r = n$.
B. $\tan \theta_r = n$.   D. $\sec \theta_r = n$.

3-12. In general, optical materials made of glasses are less expensive than those of crystals.
A. True.
B. False.

3-13. In general, optical materials made of crystals are larger in size than those of glasses.
A. True.
B. False.

3-14. The light-gathering power of an optical fiber is known as:
A. The second law of reflection.   C. The index of refraction.
B. The numerical aperture.   D. The f number.

3-15. The most common types of spectral filters are:
  A. Absorption and interference.
  B. Absorption and emission.
  C. Emission and reflective.
  D. Interference and dispersion.

3-16. An optical system using entirely reflective optics is known as:
  A. Mangin.
  B. Catadioptric.
  C. Dioptric.
  D. Catoptric.

3-17. How many of the following are examples of a catoptric optical system?
  A. Casseigrainian.
  B. Gregorian.
  C. Newtonian.
  D. Schmidt.

4

INFRARED DETECTORS

The main component in any infrared system is the detector. The detector is used to convert radiant energy into an electrical signal that may be used to provide a variety of desired readouts.

CHARACTERISTICS

There are many types of infrared detectors. Each type has a distinct set of operating parameters, or characteristics. Some of the more important characteristics are as follows:

Signal (S)

The signal (S) is the voltage generated by an infrared detector that is related to the infrared energy striking that detector. The signal generated by an infrared detector may vary with detector size, temperature, bias, and time constant.

Responsivity (Rv)

Responsivity (Rv) is the ratio of signal output to incident radiant flux. It is usually expressed as volts per watt and may be written as

$$Rv = \frac{S}{J} \qquad (4\text{-}1)$$

where,
Rv equals responsivity,
S equals rms voltage from detector,
J equals rms value of energy flux striking the detector.

Example—What is the responsivity of a detector that generates 2 volts when subjected to an incident radiant flux of 2 milliwatts?

Answer—From Equation 4-1,

$$Rv = \frac{2 \text{ volts}}{2 \text{ milliwatts}} = 1000 \text{ volts/watt}$$

Noise (N)

Noise (N) is the voltage generated by an infrared detector as a result of its resistance, temperature, bandwidth, and bias.

Noise is independent of signal input. There are five basic sources of electrical noise that occur in infrared detectors. These sources are as follows:

Johnson Noise—Sometimes referred to as *thermal noise*. This noise is caused by thermal fluctuations in the electrons within a resistive element. Johnson noise is independent of frequency.

Current Noise—Produced by the fluctuation in a resistive element caused by current. Current noise is inversely proportional to frequency and is sometimes referred to as $1/f$ *noise*.

Photon Noise—Caused by fluctuations in the rate at which photons arrive at the sensitive area of the detector. Photon noise is frequency dependent and follows the same curve as the frequency response of the detector.

Shot Noise—Caused by the random emission of electrons. Shot noise is frequency dependent and proportional to the responsivity of the detector.

Background Noise—Radiation originating from the detector environment induces background radiation noise. The extent of background radiation noise is dependent on the temperatures, emissivities, and geometry of such elements as the detector walls, window, and media as seen by the detector element.

Temperature

Some infrared detectors are mounted on thermoelectric bases or in Dewars for operation at temperature below normal ambient of 295 K (approx. 70°F).

Cooling the detector decreases its noise voltage and therefore increases its S/N ratio and detectivity. Some common operating temperatures for Dewar mounted detectors are:

> 195 K—carbon dioxide   (−78°C)
>
> 77 K—liquid nitrogen   (−196°C)
>
> 4 K—liquid helium   (−269°C)

Signal-to-Noise Ratio (S/N)

The S/N ratio is the ratio of signal to noise. The higher the S/N ratio, the better the detector.

Noise Equivalent Input (NEI)

The noise equivalent input (NEI) is the amount of incident radiation (measured in watts per square centimeter) on an infrared detector that will produce a signal/noise ratio of 1 (unity). Mathematically,

$$NEI = \frac{JN}{S} \qquad (4\text{-}2)$$

where,

J equals rms incident energy flux,
N equals rms noise voltage,
S equals rms signal voltage.

Noise Equivalent Power (NEP)

The noise equivalent power (NEP) is similar to NEI except the incident energy is measured in watts rather than watts per square centimeter. It may be expressed as

$$NEP = \frac{JNA}{S} \qquad (4\text{-}3)$$

where,

NEP equals noise equivalent power in watts,
J equals rms incident energy flux in watts per square centimeter,
N equals rms noise voltage,
S equals rms signal voltage,
A equals area of detector element.

Example—What will the rms signal voltage be from a detector with a NEP of 1.5×10^{-9} watt, a detector size of 0.1 centimeter by 0.1 centimeter, a rms noise voltage of 2 microvolts, and subjected to an rms energy flux of 3 microwatts per square centimeter?

Answer—From Equation 4-3,

$$1.5 \times 10^{-9} = \frac{3 \times 10^{-6}\,\text{W/cm}^2 \times 2 \times 10^{-6}\,\text{V} \times 1 \times 10^{-2}\,\text{cm}^2}{S}$$

$$S = \frac{6 \times 10^{-14}}{1.5 \times 10^{-9}} = 4 \times 10^{-5}\,\text{volts}$$

$$S = 40\ \text{microvolts}$$

Detectivity (D)

The detectivity (D) is the reciprocal of NEP, or

$$D = \frac{1}{NEP} \qquad (4\text{-}4)$$

The detectivity D^* (called D-star) is a figure of merit used to determine the quality of infrared detectors. D^* is normalized to unit areas and unit bandwidth. It is measured in centimeters per watt. Mathematically,

$$D* = \frac{(A\Delta f)^{1/2}}{\text{NEP}} \qquad (4\text{-}5)$$

where,

A equals area of detector element in centimeters,
Δf equals noise bandwidth in hertz,
NEP equals noise equivalent power in watts.

Example—What is the $D*$ of an infrared detector with an NEP of 5×10^{-10} W, a detector element size of 1 sq cm and a noise bandwidth of 25 Hz?

Answer—From Equation 4-5,

$$D* = \frac{(1 \text{ cm}^2\; 25 \text{ Hz})^{1/2}}{5 \times 10^{-10} \text{ W}} = \frac{5 \text{ cm}}{5 \times 10^{-10} \text{ W}}$$

$$D* = 1 \times 10^{-10} \text{ cm/W}$$

Detectivity is sometimes expressed as $D*$ (500 K, 90, 1), where 500 K is the blackbody temperature used to measure $D*$, 90 is the frequency at which the infrared radiation was modulated, and 1 the bandwidth used to measure noise (in hertz).

Time Constant (τ)

A time constant is the time required for a signal to build up to 63 percent of its maximum. The frequency response of an infrared detector is dependent on its time constant.

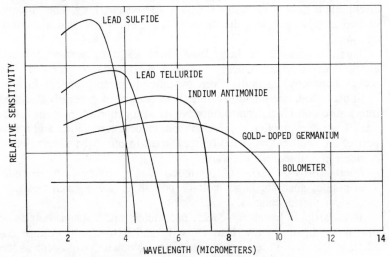

Fig. 4-1. Response curves for various infrared detectors.

Spectral Response (Rλ)

Different types of infrared detectors respond differently to various wavelengths of incident radiation. Fig. 4-1 shows some typical spectral response curves for some of the more popular types of infrared detectors.

TYPES OF DETECTORS

Infrared detectors fall into two major categories: thermal and quantum detectors.

Operation of the thermal detector is based on the change of a physical property (such as resistance or thermoelectric force) of the detector as its own temperature is changed. Some common examples of thermal detectors are themocouples, pneumatic detectors, and bolometers.

A quantum detector is a semiconductor that produces a signal proportional to the photon flux that strikes its sensitive element. Quantum detectors include photoconductive, photovoltaic, and photoelectromagnetic (PEM) detectors.

In general, thermal detectors have a uniform spectral response but exhibit a longer time constant than quantum detectors.

Thermal Detectors

The following devices are examples of common thermal detectors.

Thermocouple—When two dissimilar metals are connected and heat is applied to one of the junctions, electrons will flow through the circuit. This flow of electrons is called *thermoelectricity*. The junction of two metals exhibiting the thermoelectric effect is called a *thermocouple*.

Thermocouples have been used since 1830 to convert thermal energy into electrical energy. Typical thermocouple materials are nickel, antimony, bismuth, silver, metallic alloys and semiconductors.

In operation, one junction of the thermocouple is generally flattened into a disc and blackened to improve its absorption of incident radiation. The other junction is shielded from incoming radiation and forms part of an electrical balanced-bridge circuit to offset the effects due to changes in ambient temperature.

Thermopile—A series of thermocouples is called a *thermopile*. Thermopiles generate larger voltage potentials, for a given temperature, than thermocouples.

Metal Strip Bolometers—Metal bolometers are blackened strips of thin metal having a low heat capacity and a high temperature coefficient. Changes in resistance across the bolometer strip occur as the incident energy is changed.

Fig. 4-2. Thermistor bolometers.

Thermistor Bolometer—The thermistor is a thermal-sensitive resistor. Fig. 4-2 shows various thermistor bolometers. The active element in a thermistor bolometer is a thin semiconductor film usually composed of oxide mixtures of manganese, nickel, and cobalt.

The thermistor "flake" is usually attached to a heat-conducting thermal sink to increase its response time.

Fig. 4-3 shows a normal bolometer bridge circuit. The thermistor flakes (T_1 and T_2) are identical and mounted on a common base to

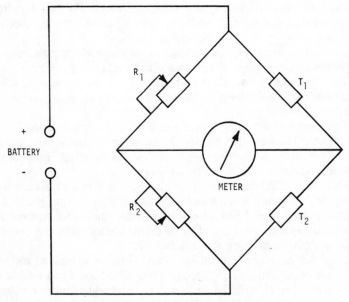

Fig. 4-3. Bolometer bridge circuit.

compensate for errors caused by changes in ambient temperature. Thermistor T_1 is exposed to radiant energy, while thermistor T_2 is shielded from outside radiation. Resistors R_1 and R_2 are used to balance the circuit when thermistors T_1 and T_2 are at the same temperature. When infrared radiation is focused onto T_1, the resistance of T_1 will change, causing current to flow. The amount and direction of meter deflections is related to the amount of infrared energy striking thermistor T_1.

Golay Cell—The golay cell is a pneumatic detector containing a small xenon-filled chamber. Infrared energy entering the cell is directed to a radiation-absorbing film or membrane. An increase in temperature of the membrane expands the gas and causes a flexible mirror to distort or defocus light energy being reflected onto a photocell. The change in light intensity striking the photocell is related to the expansion of the gas, which is related to the incoming infrared radiation.

Ferroelectric Bolometer—Made of barium-strontium titanate, the ferroelectric bolometer is essentially a temperature-sensitive capacitor. The ferroelectric bolometer produces an electrical signal functionally related to the capacitor dielectric temperature and, in turn, to the thermal radiation incident on, and absorbed by, the device.

Quantum Detectors

Quantum detectors are semiconductors that essentially count the amount of photons striking a sensitive element. Photons striking a quantum detector interact with the crystal lattice, freeing electrons or holes.

There are three photon detection techniques: photoconductive, photovoltaic, and photoelectromagnetic (PEM).

The photoconductive effect is the increase in electrical conductivity of a semiconductor caused by an increase in free carriers produced by incident radiation.

The photovoltaic effect takes place at a pn junction in a semiconductor. Photons striking the junction cause hole-electron pairs to diffuse in opposite directions across the junction, producing a charge separation and therefore a voltage.

The PEM effect is also a diffusion phenomenon that occurs when radiation falls upon a semiconductor that is within a magnetic field.

Photovoltaic and PEM detectors generate their own voltage that is related to radiation incident upon them. Photoconductive detectors require a bias to produce a signal voltage.

Lead Sulfide—The lead sulfide (PbS) detector is perhaps the most common of all infrared photoconductive detectors. Lead sulfide detectors may be chemically deposited or evaporated onto a subtrate (usually quartz). (See Fig. 4-4A.) Lead sulfide detectors may be

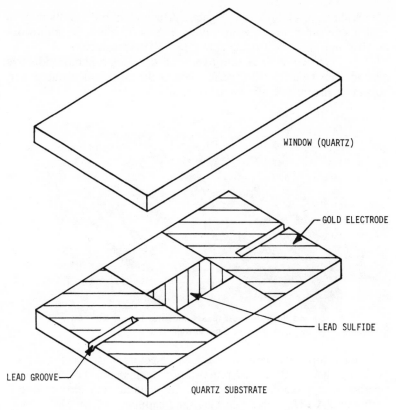

WINDOW (QUARTZ)

GOLD ELECTRODE

LEAD SULFIDE

LEAD GROOVE

QUARTZ SUBSTRATE

(A) On the substrate.

Courtesy Infrared Industries, Inc.

(B) Complete detector.

Fig. 4-4. Lead sulfide detector.

operated at room temperatures or may be cooled to increase their S/N ratios. Fig. 4-4B is a photograph of a cooled photoconductive PbS infrared detector.

Lead Selenide—Lead Selenide (PbSe) detectors are photoconductive and may be produced in much the same way as lead sulfide.

Indium Antimonide—Perhaps the most versatile of all infrared detectors, indium antimonide (InSb) may be used as a photoconductive, photovoltaic, or photoelectromagnetic detector. InSb detectors may be cooled or used at room temperature. Fig. 4-5 shows the photoconductive and photoelectromagnetic types of InSb detectors.

Doped Germanium—A sensitive, long-wavelength photoconductive detector may be made using germanium as the host semiconductor and copper or mercury as the impurity atoms.

Fig. 4-5. InSb detectors: photoconductive type at left, PEM type at right.

Copper-doped germanium (Cu:Ge) detectors must operate at temperatures below 10 K. Mercury-doped germanium (Hg:Ge) may operate at temperatures up to 40 K. Germanium may also be doped with gold (Au:Ge), zinc (Zn:Ge), and cadmium (Cd:Ge).

Mercury Cadmium Telluride—Mercury cadmium telluride (HgCdTe) detectors are photoconductive and operate at a temperature of 77 K.

Table 4-1 lists the more important characteristics of the various types of infrared detectors that have been described.

Fig. 4-6. InSb detector array.

Table 4-1. Characteristics of Infrared Detectors

Detector	Mode of Operation	Operating Temperature (K)	Peak Response (λ)	Cutoff (λ)	Time Constant	D* Typical (Peak)
PbS	PC	295	2.1	2.5	250μs	10^{11}
PbS	PC	193	2.5	3.0	450μs	2×10^{11}
PbS	PC	77	2.5	3.3	450μs	8×10^{10}
PbSe	PC	295	3.4	4.2	5μs	7×10^8
PbSe	PC	193	4.6	5.4	30μs	6×10^9
InSb	PC	295	6.5	7.3	0.2μs	4×10^7
InSb	PC	193	5.0	6.1	1μs	8×10^9
InSb	PC	77	5.0	5.4	2μs	6×10^{10}
InSb	PV	77	5.3	5.6	1μs	4×10^{10}
InSb	PEM	295	6.2	7.0	0.2μs	3×10^8
Au:Ge	PC	77	4.7	6.9	1μs	4×10^{10}
Zn:Ge	PC	4	36	40	0.01μs	10^{10}
Cu:Ge	PC	20	20	27	2.3μs	3×10^{10}
HgCdTe	PC	77	10	15	1μs	10^{10}
Thermistor Bolometer	Bolo-meter	295	Black	Black	1ms	2×10^8
Radiation Thermocouple	Thermo-electric	295	Black	Black	40ms	10^9
Golay Cell		295	Black	Black	20ms	2×10^9
Ferroelectric Bolometer	Ferro-electric	295	Black	Black	1ms	10^9

Detector Arrays

Infrared detectors may be constructed in linear arrays or matrices using hundreds of individual detectors closely spaced and in a wide variety of configurations (Fig. 4-6).

Bicells or quadcells, consisting of two or four sections, are used for position-sensing applications. The signal out of such a detector is related to the position of incident radiation relative to the center of the cell.

Linear arrays may be used for single-line infrared scanning systems. Area arrays are commonly used for two-dimensional scan techniques. No moving optics are needed when detector arrays are used making scanning systems more rugged and reliable.

Area arrays of infrared detectors may be used to make infrared vidicon tubes for infrared television systems.

QUESTIONS

4-1. Responsivity may be expressed as:
A. Signal/noise.
B. Watts/volt.
C. Volts/watt.
D. Volts/signal.

4-2. Which is the correct formula for noise equivalent power (NEP)?
A. S/N.
C. $S/(N \times JNA)$.
B. JNA/S.
D. JNS/A.

4-3. Detectivity (D^*) may be expressed as:
A. $1/JN$.
C. $1/NEP$.
B. $(A\Delta f)^{1/2}/NEP$.
D. $1/NEI$.

4-4. What are the two major classes of infrared detectors?
A. Quantum and photon.
C. Thermal and quantum.
B. Thermal and photoconductive.
D. Photoconductive and photovoltaic.

4-5. Which type of infrared detector requires a magnetic field for its operation?
A. Photovoltaic.
C. Photoconductive.
B. Thermal.
D. Photoelectromagnetic.

4-6. In general, quantum detectors have a faster response time than thermal detectors.
A. True.
B. False.

4-7. In general, thermal detectors are "black," that is, they respond equally to all infrared wavelengths.
A. True.
B. False.

4-8. The signal-to-noise ratio of many infrared detectors may be enhanced by cooling the detector.
A. True.
B. False.

4-9. The best detector to use for detection of 2.5-micrometer radiation is:
A. PbS.
C. InSb.
B. PbSe.
D. Thermistor bolometer.

4-10. Which of the following detectors cannot be used for detection of 5-micrometer radiation?
A. InSb.
C. PbS.
B. Thermistor bolometer.
D. CuGe.

5

INSTRUMENTATION

This chapter deals with infrared instrumentation devices: radiometers, thermometers, sources, collimators, comparators, modulators, and spectroscopes.

RADIOMETERS

An infrared radiometer is a device used to measure the amount of thermal energy radiated by a substance. The radiometer is the most common and most basic of all infrared instruments and systems. There are many types and designs of infrared radiometers but they all contain the same basic components. Fig. 5-1 shows a modern infrared radiometer. The electronics unit is at the left, the radiometer head at the right.

Basic Radiometer

Fig. 5-2 shows a simplified block diagram of a typical infrared radiometer. The solid blocks in Fig. 5-2 indicate the components, or circuits, required for a basic radiometer. The remaining blocks indicate additional circuits that may be added to increase the instrument's overall abilities.

Optical System—Optical systems are used to collect and focus the infrared energy into the detector. The optical system acts as an amplifier since it permits the relatively small infrared detector to "see" higher levels of infrared radiation.

Optical systems may be refractive or reflective, or simple or complex, depending on the application. Major considerations in choice of optical systems are wavelengths to be measured and field of view, which depends on target size and distance. The operating environment of the radiometer should also be considered in determining the correct optical systems.

Glass windows or lenses would not be used to measure radiation at 10 micrometers since glass is opaque at wavelengths beyond 3 micrometers. A better choice would be arsenic trisulfide, sodium chloride, or an all-reflective optical system.

The field of view of the radiometer is determined by its optical system and the size of the detector element used. A distant target must be completely resolved (fill the radiometer field of view) to be properly measured. The field of view may be determined by

$$\tan \theta = \frac{l_d}{f} \qquad (5\text{-}1)$$

where,
θ equals field of view in degrees,
l_d equals length of one side of a square detector,
f equals focal length of optical system.

NOTE: For small angles, $\tan \theta$ is approximately equal to the angle in radians.

Example—What is the field of view of an optical system having a focal length of 25 mm and a detector size of 1 mm by 1 mm?

Answer—From Equation 5-1,

$$\tan \theta = \frac{1}{25} = 0.04$$

$$\theta = 0.04 \text{ radian, or } 2° 18'$$

Fig. 5-1. Infrared radiometer.

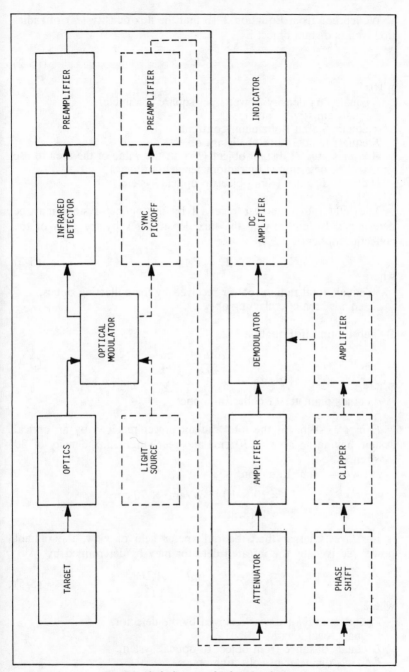

Fig. 5-2. Block diagram of infrared radiometer.

We learned from Equation 2-13 that the flux density (F) of radiation from a distant object is

$$F = \frac{\epsilon \sigma T^4 A}{\pi D^2}$$ (5-2)

where,

F equals flux density in watts per square centimeter,
ϵ equals emissivity factor,
σ equals Stefan-Boltzmann constant,
T equals temperature of distant object,
A equals area of distant object (NOTE: the value of the area to use will be determined by radiometer field of view),
D equals distance from object to optical system.

The total radiant power received by the optical system may be determined by multiplying the flux density (F) by the area of the collecting optics:

$$P_o = F A_o$$ (5-3)

where,

P_o equals total radiant power received by the collecting optics,
A_o equals area of collecting optics.

By substitution in Equation 5-2,

$$P_o = \frac{\epsilon \sigma T^4 A}{\pi D^2} \times \frac{\pi d^2}{4}$$ (5-4)

where,

d equals diameter of collecting optics.

Example—What is the total radiant power received by an optical system having an area of 70 cm² and receiving a flux density of 20 mW/cm²?

Answer—From Equation 5-3,

$$P_o = 20 \times 10^{-3} \text{ W/cm}^2 \times 70 \text{ cm}^2$$
$$= 1.4 \text{ watts}$$

For targets larger than the radiometer field of view, the radiant power received by the infrared detector may be determined by

$$P_d = \frac{\epsilon \sigma T^4}{\pi D^2} \times \frac{\pi d^2}{4} \times \frac{A_d D^2}{f^2}$$ (5-5)

where,

P_d equals radiant power received by the detector,
f equals focal length,
D equals distance from object to optical system,
d equals diameter of collecting optics,
A_d equals area of detector.

All other terms are as indicated in Equation 5-2.

It should be noted that for a resolved target or larger, the distance (D) from the optical system to the target does not influence the power received by the detector.

Equation 5-5 becomes

$$P_d = \frac{\epsilon \sigma T^4 d^2 A_d}{4f^2} \qquad (5\text{-}6)$$

We learned in Equation 2-5 that the radiant energy (W) emitted by an object was equal to $\epsilon \sigma T^4$. Therefore

$$P_d = \frac{W_d^2 A_d}{4f^2} \qquad (5\text{-}7)$$

Example—How much radiant power will be received from a target emitting 0.1 W/cm² by a detector 1 mm by 1 mm in an optical system with a focal length of 20 cm and a diameter of 30 cm?

Answer—From Equation 5-7,

$$P_d = \frac{0.1 \text{ W } (30 \text{ cm})^2 \, 0.01 \text{ cm}^2}{\text{cm}^2 \, 4 \, (20 \text{ cm})^2} = \frac{0.9 \text{ W}}{1.6 \times 10^3}$$
$$= 5.6 \times 10^{-4} \text{ W}$$

It should be noted that the infrared detector chosen for the radiometer must have a noise equivalent power (NEP) of less than the total radiant power (P_d) expected to be received by the detector.

The following list, based on Equation 5-7, shows what changes are required to increase the radiant power received by the infrared detector:

1. Increase the target temperature,
2. Increase the area of the collecting optics,
3. Increase the area of the detector element, or
4. Decrease the focal length of the optical system.

Modulator—The infrared detector in a radiometer normally looks at a target that has a constant or slow-changing temperature. This results in a very-low-level dc signal from the detector which is difficult to amplify. Detector outputs of a few microvolts (10^{-6} volt) are common.

A chopper blade may be used to modulate the incoming radiation at a fixed frequency. This produces an ac signal which is easier to amplify. The maximum frequency that should be used is determined by the time constant of the detector and may be expressed as

$$f_{max} = \frac{1}{2\pi t} \qquad (5\text{-}8)$$

where,

f_{max} equals maximum operating frequency in hertz,
t equals time constant in seconds.

Example—What is the maximum chopping frequency that should be used for a PbS detector with a time constant of 500 microseconds?
Answer—From Equation 5-8,

$$f_{max} = \frac{1}{6.28 \times 5 \times 10^{-4}}$$
$$= 318 \text{ hertz}$$

The chopper disc (Fig. 5-3) is normally placed between the collecting optics and the detector. The chopper disc is kept at a minimum size by placing it as close to the detector as possible.

Courtesy Sylvania Electric Products, Inc.
Fig. 5-3. Chopping disc.

A synchronous motor is generally used to rotate the chopper blade. The number of blades (or openings) on the disc and the speed of the motor determines the chopping (or modulation) frequency. Mathematically,

$$f_{ch} = \frac{\text{rpm} \times N_o}{60} \qquad (5\text{-}9)$$

where,

f_{ch} equals modulation frequency in hertz,
rpm equals revolutions per minute of motor,
N_o equals number of openings in chopper disc.

72

Example—What is the modulation frequency of a chopper disc with 10 openings and driven by an 1800-rpm motor?

Answer—From Equation 5-9,

$$f_{ch} = \frac{1800 \times 10}{60} = 300 \text{ hertz}$$

Chopping of the incoming radiation is not necessary (and may be undesirable) in radiometers that are used to observe rapid-changing thermal transients. For example, a 10-microsecond thermal transient may occur at the instant the chopper blade (rather than the chopper opening) is blocking the detector field of view. Fig. 5-4 shows the chopper as it is in the optical head of the radiometer.

Fig. 5-4. Internal view of radiometer optics.

Vibrating reeds and tuning forks may also be used to modulate the incoming radiation at fixed or variable frequencies.

Infrared Detector—The infrared detector is the "heart" of a radiometer. It must be chosen with care. Major considerations for final choice of a detector are spectral response, time constant, and NEP. Other considerations include environmental conditions and type of bias required (if any).

The detector alternately "sees" the energy emitted from the chopper blade and then the energy emitted from the target. In this case the chopper-blade temperature becomes the reference level. The amplitude of the ac signal from the detector is related to the difference between the temperature of the chopper blade and that of the target.

In some cases the detector may be mounted in a thermally stable chamber for increased stability or sensitivity. Cooling at constant temperatures may be achieved by mounting the detector in a Dewar flask or on a thermoelectric cooler. Heating is accomplished by mounting the detector element in a heated surface or by placing the detector in a temperature-controlled oven.

Bias Supply—Photoconductive detectors and bolometers require an external dc bias for proper operation. Detector bias supplies must be regulated and well filtered. Any slight change in bias amplitude will show up as a signal from the detector. It is common to use batteries for detector bias, especially when signal levels will be in microvolts.

Photovoltaic and photoelectromagnetic (PEM) detectors do not require external bias supplies.

Preamplifier—The radiometer preamplifier is normally placed as close as possible to the infrared detector. Radiometer preamplifiers are extremely stable, low-noise, wide-band preamplifiers.

Input circuits vary from transformer coupling for low-impedance detectors (such as the InSb PEM) to direct or capacitor coupling for higher-impedance detectors.

The preamplifier output is generally from a low-impedance source (such as cathode or emitter followers) so that the signal may be transmitted through a cable to the main electronic control unit, which is normally separated from the optical assembly.

Amplifier—The main amplifier, or thermal amplifier, is a typical audio-type amplifier which usually contains attenuator switches or gain controls. When a chopper disc is used in the radiometer, the amplifier may have circuits tuned to the modulating frequency to minimize any "noise" that may have entered the signal channel.

Demodulator—The amplified ac signal is converted to a dc signal at the demodulator stage. The resultant dc signal is related to the target temperature and may be used to drive any number of displays or readouts.

Display—The display, or presentation, of the amplified signal depends upon the application of the radiometer. Readout devices may include meters, pen recorders, and oscilloscopes.

The readout devices may be calibrated in temperature or energy. Meter readouts requiring the use of conversion tables are quite common.

Optional Features

The following are features which may be incorporated into infrared radiometers, though it is not necessary that they be thus included.

Synchronous Detection—Fig. 5-5 shows the electrical signals generated by an infrared detector sensing targets at three different temperatures.

Since the detector references the chopper-blade temperature to the target temperature, it is possible for two different temperatures to generate a signal of the same amplitude.

Consider the case as referenced in Fig. 5-5A. A target at a temperature of 34°C will not produce any ac signal from the detector if the chopper-blade temperature is also at 34°C.

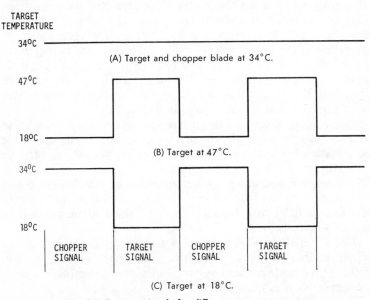

TARGET
TEMPERATURE

34°C

(A) Target and chopper blade at 34°C.

47°C

18°C

(B) Target at 47°C.

34°C

18°C

| CHOPPER SIGNAL | TARGET SIGNAL | CHOPPER SIGNAL | TARGET SIGNAL |

(C) Target at 18°C.

Fig. 5-5. Detector signals for different target temperatures.

If the target temperature should increase to 47°C then an ac signal of some specific amplitude will be produced (Fig. 5-5B). If the target temperature decreases to 18°C then an ac signal of the same amplitude will be produced (Fig. 5-5C). However, the phase of the ac signal produced by the colder temperature would be shifted by 180°. It is important therefore to know the phase of the target signal to distinguish between "hot" and "cold" targets.

A synchronous signal may be used to determine phase of the thermal signal. The synchronous signal is usually generated by the chopper blade so that the frequencies of the thermal signal and the synchronous signal will be the same.

Placing a magnetic pickoff coil near the chopper blade induces an electrical signal as each blade opening passes the coil. If the chopper blade is made of a nonmagnetic material, a light source and photocell may be used to obtain the "sync" signal. Optical sync signals are obtained by reflecting the light source off the chopper blade or by "chopping" the light beam.

The sync signal is then amplified by conventional techniques. A phase-shift network is sometimes used to ensure proper phase relationship between the sync signal and the thermal signal. A limiting, or clipping, stage is often used to provide a constant-amplitude sync signal that is fed into a phase detector or demodulator for comparison to the variable-amplitude thermal signal from the target.

Regardless of what the radiometer is aimed at, the sync signal will always be of constant amplitude and phase. The thermal signal will change in amplitude or phase (or both) depending upon the target temperature. If the temperature of the target is the same as that of the chopper blade then no ac signal will be present in the thermal amplifier. However, since a sync signal is still present, we will get a dc voltage from the synchronous phase detector. For the sake of comparison, let's assume that the dc voltage is +10 volts.

If the radiometer senses a target having a temperature greater than that of its chopper blade, the thermal signal will be in phase with the sync signal and will add to it, producing an output voltage of more than +10 volts.

If the target temperature is lower than that of the chopper blade, the two signals at the synchronous demodulator will be 180° out of phase and partially cancel each other. The resultant output will be less than +10 volts.

Internal Reference—When viewing targets having similar energy levels as that of the chopper blade it becomes important that the temperature of the blade remain constant. Temperature control of a moving chopper blade is quite difficult.

An internal-reference source may be added to most radiometers. Two common internal-reference configurations are shown in Fig. 5-6. In both techniques the chopper blade must have a highly reflective surface. The detector alternately "sees" the target and then the constant-temperature reference source.

The in-line reference source (Fig. 5-6A) uses a blackbody cavity with the detector at, or near, the apex of the cavity. Optical relay techniques may be used to physically place the infrared detector away from the heated reference cavity.

The off-axis reference source (Fig. 5-6B) is usually a blackbody cavity but may be most any constant-temperature source, provided internal reflections are at a minimum and also at constant temperatures.

Built-in Calibration—The accuracy of any instrument depends somewhat upon its calibration. Radiometers are generally calibrated in the laboratory by use of blackbody radiation sources.

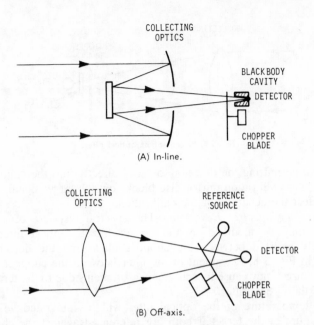

(A) In-line.

(B) Off-axis.

Fig. 5-6. Internal-reference configurations.

In many radiometer applications it is impractical to use laboratory calibration techniques. For this reason, some radiometers have a built-in calibration source. Ideally, the calibration source should be a blackbody cavity; however, other types of constant-temperature sources such as tungsten filaments, Nernst glowers, and globars may be used. Fig. 5-7 shows a simplified optical schematic of a radiometer using an internal calibration source.

In normal use the radiometer "sees" the target as shown in Fig. 5-7 (normal position of the mirror). When the internal calibration source is activated, a solenoid moves the calibration mirror to the calibrate

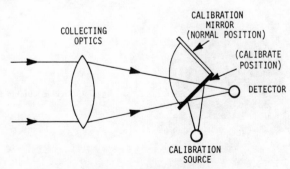

Fig. 5-7. Radiometer with internal calibration source.

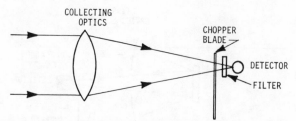

COLLECTING OPTICS

CHOPPER BLADE

DETECTOR

FILTER

Fig. 5-8. Placement of optical filter.

position, permitting the detector to "see" directly into the calibration source. The calibration mirror also blocks out the target signal, which may effect the accuracy of the calibration.

Filters for Spectral Response—The spectral response of a radiometer may be modified by the use of filters. Optical filters are normally inserted between the chopper blade and the detector as shown in Fig. 5-8. Placement of the filter between the chopper blade and the target may cause inaccurate measurements due to the temperature of the optical filter.

The temperature of the optical filter will be integrated with the temperature of the target if both are referenced against the chopper blade, or internal reference. When the optical filter is placed between the chopper blade and the infrared detector, the temperature of the optical filter generates a dc signal that is not modulated and therefore not amplified.

Optical filters may be individually inserted as required or mounted on manually or automatically controlled filter wheels. In addition, circular variable filters are now available providing continuously adjustable, narrow-wavelength response. Fig. 5-9 shows a circular variable filter in two segments for 2.8 to 5.6 micrometers and 7 to 14 micrometers.

Interchangeable Detectors—Spectral response may also be modified by use of interchangeable infrared detectors.

Fig. 5-9. Circular variable filter.

Courtesy Exotech, Inc.

Fig. 5-10. Dual-channel radiometer.

Multichannel Radiometer—At times it may be desirable to observe a distant target with more than one spectral bandwidth. This is especially true when observing a phenomenon lasting only for a short duration. Instead of using two or more radiometers, it is possible to use a common optical system and two or more signal-processing channels having different spectral responses. Fig. 5-10 shows such a radiometer.

Fig. 5-11 shows the optical configurations of two types of multichannel radiometers. In Fig. 5-11A two detectors are used with a common chopper blade allowing for only one modulation frequency. If the two detectors to be used have greatly different response times then two separate chopper blades must be used as shown in Fig. 5-11B. In this case the thermistor bolometer is modulated at 30 hertz and the indium antimonide detector is modulated at 600 hertz.

The radiation-directing system in Fig. 5-11B may be a beam-splitting mirror transmitting half of the incoming radiation and reflecting the other half; or it may be a rapidly rotating front-surfaced mirror that alternately directs the incoming radiation to the two infrared detectors.

Emissivity Adjustment—Two objects at the same temperature may emit different amounts of radiation, depending on the emissivity value of the objects. If the emissivity value of an object is known, it is possible to correct the radiometer signal to read actual temperature or equivalent blackbody energy. The technique to compensate for errors due to emissivity is quite simple. It requires the use of a gain control that is calibrated in emissivity.

A blackbody at 1600°F will emit about 10 W/cm². This will be converted by the radiometer to an electrical signal of some value. For convenience, let us place this value at 10 volts.

Now, an object at 1600°F having an emissivity of 0.5 will emit 5 W/cm² (0.5 × 10). This in turn will generate only 5 volts from the radiometer (all other conditions being equal). Therefore, to compensate for the loss of signal due to emissivity we must increase the gain of the radiometer amplifier by two. This will give us the 10 volts needed to indicate 10 W/cm² (for equivalent blackbody radiation) or 1600°F (for actual temperature). Table 5-1 shows the gain required for various emissivity settings.

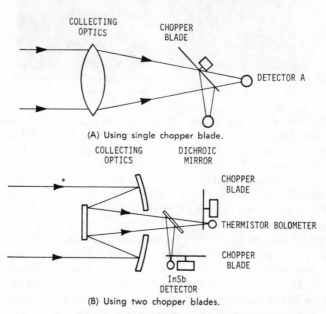

(A) Using single chopper blade.

(B) Using two chopper blades.

Fig. 5-11. Optics of multichannel radiometer.

Table 5-1. Gain Required for Emissivity Settings

Emissivity Setting	Required Gain
1.0	1.0
0.9	1.11
0.8	1.25
0.7	1.43
0.6	1.66
0.5	2.0
0.4	2.5
0.3	3.33
0.2	5.0
0.1	10.0
0.05	20.0

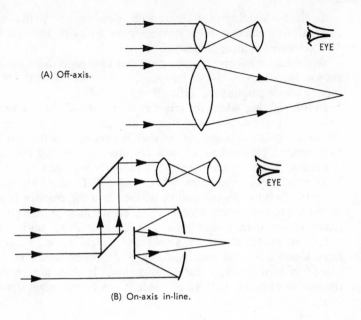

(A) Off-axis.

(B) On-axis in-line.

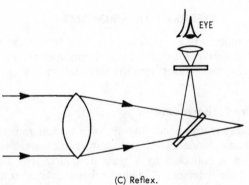

(C) Reflex.

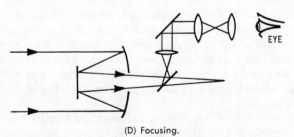

(D) Focusing.

Fig. 5-12. Sighting methods.

Sighting—Sighting of a target with a radiometer is like aiming a camera. Any number of techniques may be used. Fig. 5-12 shows four common sighting techniques.

A sighting telescope may be mounted alongside the radiometer as shown in 5-12A. This is inexpensive and satisfactory for distant targets where parallax has little effect.

In-line sighting, where the target optical axis and the sighting optical axis are the same, provides greater alignment accuracy. Fig. 5-12B shows an in-line sighting system that is easy to add to most existing radiometers. This technique, however, does not permit the viewer to determine if the detector optics are properly focused.

The techniques shown in 5-12C and 5-12D allow the viewer to focus the target to his eye and be assured that the detector is properly focused. (Except where focusing is accomplished by moving the detector rather than the optics). The beam-splitting mirror used in 5-12C attenuates the target signal and should be used only where large signal levels are anticipated. The alignment mirror in 5-12D is placed in position only during alignment. It does not permit continuous monitoring of the target since it blocks the target signal when in use.

INFRARED THERMOMETERS

Infrared thermometers are radiometers used for temperature measurement and control. Most infrared thermometers are relatively simple compared with more sophisticated laboratory and military radiometers.

Typical Infrared Thermometer

Fig. 5-13 shows a simplified diagram of a typical radiometer used for general-purpose, noncontact, temperature measurement. The incoming radiation is collected by a glass or quartz lens and focused onto a lead sulfide detector. A dichroic beam-splitter transmits the visible signal to the on-axis sighting optics and also deflects the infrared energy to the detector. A fixed-frequency chopper blade driven by a synchronous motor modulates the incoming radiation at about 300 hertz. Focusing from a few feet to infinity is accomplished by moving the lens along the optical axis. The target is focused onto an image screen that is at the same distance from the lens as that of the detector. The image screen usually contains a reticle that defines the radiometer field of view so that the user knows whether or not the target is resolved.

Spectral response of this type of radiometer is usually from 1.0 to 2.7 micrometers. Within this spectral band, temperatures as low as 200°F can be detected. Extremely high temperatures will require the

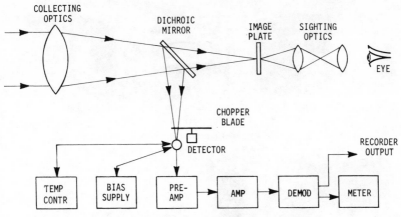

Fig. 5-13. Radiometer for temperature measurement.

use of optical attenuators to prevent the detector from saturating or heating.

The lead sulfide detector is heated to a temperature of at least 130°F for stability and for reliable operation in ambient temperatures up to the detector control temperature.

Specifications of a typical infrared thermometer are as follows:

Temperature Range:	200°F to 5000°F
Temperature Accuracy:	2% of temperature
Temperature Sensitivity:	0.5% of temperature
Temperature Repeatability:	0.5% of temperature
Focusing Range:	10 inches to infinity
Field of View:	1°
Response Time:	0.5 second
Spectral Response:	1.0 to 2.7 micrometers
Emissivity Range:	0.2 to 1.0

Fig. 5-14A shows a photograph of a typical infrared thermometer. The optical head is connected to the combination power supply and control unit by a cable that may be over 100 feet in length.

A low-cost, hand-held, battery-operated infrared thermometer is shown in Fig. 5-14B. It has a fixed focus at about 10 feet and can resolve a target of 1 inch diameter.

Optical Pyrometer

Prior to the development of the infrared radiometer, the optical pyrometer was the only noncontact temperature-measuring device available. A simplified optical schematic of the optical pyrometer is shown in Fig. 5-15.

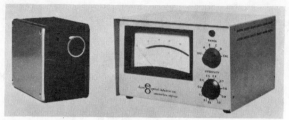

Courtesy Electro Optical Industries, Inc.

(A) Typical unit.

(B) Portable unit.

Courtesy Raytek, Inc.

Fig. 5-14. Infrared thermometers.

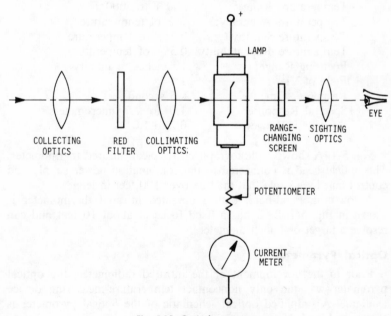

Fig. 5-15. Optical pyrometer.

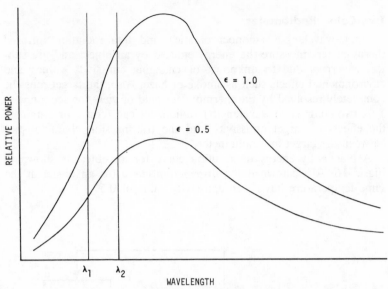

Fig. 5-16. Energy distribution curves.

The optical pyrometer is a color-matching device and only usable for objects hot enough to emit visible energy (about 1100°F). In operation, the user sights the optical pyrometer onto the target. The color of the target is imaged against the filament of the pyrometer lamp. Current is varied through the filament until its color matches the target color. The current readout device is calibrated in equivalent temperature rather than current. Temperature accuracies of better than 0.1°C are obtainable.

The optical pyrometer is not a continuous readout device and cannot be used for temperature control.

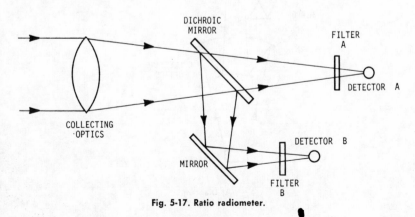

Fig. 5-17. Ratio radiometer.

Two-Color Radiometer

Single-wavelength (monochromatic) and total-radiation infrared thermometers measure the energy emitted by an object and are subject to errors due to unknown or changing emissivity values and environmental effects such as smoke or haze. Also, the target must be completely resolved by the thermometer field of view for accuracy.

A two-color (two-wavelength) radiometer can reduce or eliminate the effects of target emissivity and the transmission characteristics between the target and radiometer.

A blackbody energy distribution curve for an object is shown in Fig. 5-16. Also shown is the distribution curve for an object at the same temperature having an emissivity value of 0.5.

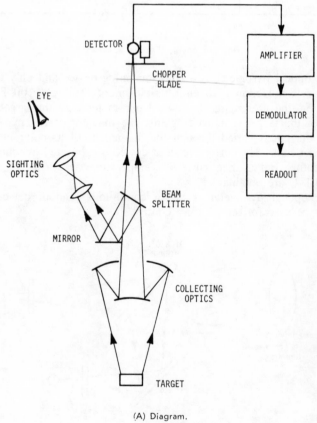

(A) Diagram.

Fig. 5-18.

If we were to measure the energy emitted at two given wavelengths (λ_1 and λ_2) we would find that a 1000°F blackbody emits 0.31 W/cm^2/μm at 2.5 μm (λ_2) and 0.11 W/cm^2/μm at 1.8 μm (λ_1). Now consider the ratio between these two energy levels:

$$R_t = \frac{W_{\lambda_1}}{W_{\lambda_2}} \qquad (5\text{-}10)$$

where,

R_t equals ratio (apparent temperature),

W_{λ_1} equals energy emitted at λ_1,

W_{λ_2} energy emitted at λ_2.

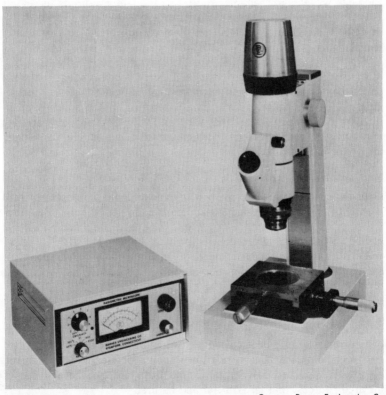

Courtesy Barnes Engineering Co.

(B) Photograph.

Radiometric microscope.

By substitution,

$$R_t = \frac{0.11}{0.31} = 0.355$$

If the 1000°F source were not a blackbody, but had an emissivity value of 0.5 then the energy emitted at λ_1 would be 0.055 W/cm²/μm and the energy at λ_2 would be 0.155 W/cm²/μm. Notice, however, that the ratio between λ_1 and λ_2 would still be 0.355 (0.055 ÷ 0.155). The same ratio would also be measured if there were some attenuation of the energy due to the transmitting media.

As the temperature increases, the slope of the distribution increases and the ratio between W_{λ_1} and W_{λ_2} will increase.

Both wavelengths selected for a two-color, or ratio, radiometer must be in the same slope of either side of the energy distribution curve. We learned from Wien's displacement law (Equation 2-7) that the peak wavelength becomes shorter as the temperature is increased. For a wavelength of 2.8 micrometers (λ_2) a maximum temperature of 1400°F can be measured before the need arises to select two shorter wavelengths.

Fig. 5-17 shows a simplified optical diagram of a ratio radiometer. It should be noted that the ratio radiometer depends upon the emissivity, or transmission, being constant at all wavelengths. Unfortunately, this is not always true; many materials, or transmitting mediums, have emissivity values that vary with wavelengths. This variation in wavelength will effect the ratio measured and result in an error in apparent temperature.

Radiometric Microscope

A radiometer may be used with conventional microscope techniques providing very high optical resolution for thermal measurements of extremely small areas. Fig. 5-18A is a simplified schematic of the radiometric microscope shown in Figure 5-18B. The work piece is mounted on a movable X-Y stage and may be viewed while the emitted energy is being measured.

SOURCES

Almost every thing emits infrared radiation and therefore is a source of infrared energy. For accurate measurement, however, a radiometer must be calibrated against a known source or standard of infrared energy. We learned in Chapter 2 that there are two basic types of infrared sources, that is, artificial and natural.

Artificial sources fall into three categories. They are total radiation, spectral radiation, and coherent radiation.

Fig. 5-19. 1000°C blackbody radiation source.

Total Radiation

Total-radiation sources are blackbody radiators. That is, they are perfect emitters of infrared radiation. Blackbody sources are available for temperatures from below ambient to as high as 3000°C. A typical blackbody source is shown in Fig. 5-19. It has a temperature range of 50°C to 1000°C and a cavity opening of 0.5 inch in diameter.

A simplified schematic of a typical blackbody radiator is shown in Fig. 5-20. The conical cavity is made of steel, ceramic, or graphite. An insulated heating element is wound tightly along the length of the cavity in such a manner as to eliminate any thermal gradients that may occur due to the varying mass along the cavity length.

The cavity and heating element are enclosed in a housing containing a thermal insulator such as diatomaceous earth. The housing may be water cooled.

A temperature sensing element is usually embedded in the cavity slug at or near the apex: In some instances a resistance thermometer may be interwound with the heating element.

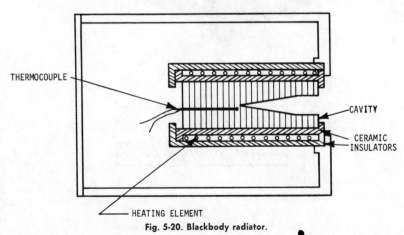

THERMOCOUPLE

CAVITY

CERAMIC INSULATORS

HEATING ELEMENT

Fig. 5-20. Blackbody radiator.

The sensed temperature is compared to a reference that is preset by the user. Any error in actual temperature to sensed temperature is amplified and fed into the heater control circuit. Temperature control may be on-off or proportional.

Some blackbody sources such as the one shown in Fig. 5-21A operate at temperatures much too high for contact-type sensing elements. In this case a radiometric probe is placed at one end of a dual-cavity slug (Fig. 5-21B).

Most blackbody sources have aperture wheels mounted in front of the cavity so that the user may vary the total amount of radiation emitted at any given temperature. Some blackbodies allow for the insertion of optical filters to generate radiation at specific wavelengths.

Courtesy Electro Optical Industries, Inc.

(A) Unit.

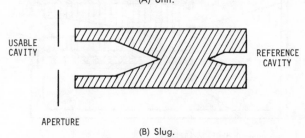

(B) Slug.

Fig. 5-21. 3000°C blackbody radiation source.

Spectral Radiation

Most sources emit energy in distinct spectral regions that are characteristic of their substance and surroundings.

Lamps of various types are quite often used as infrared sources. Some of the more popular lamps are carbon- or tungsten-filament, tungsten-quartz-halogen, mercury and xenon short-arc, cesium-vapor arc, and zirconium-oxide concentrated arc.

Tungsten lamps are often used as standards of spectral radiation. These lamps are usually calibrated against secondary standards that are traceable to the National Bureau of Standards. Calibration may be in watts per steradian (or unit area) per micrometer or brightness (or color) temperature in kelvins. Fig. 5-22 shows a modern thermal light source.

Fig. 5-22. Thermal light source.

Courtesy Cintra, Inc.

The spectral range of a tungsten filament within a quartz envelope is about 0.25 to 2.5 micrometers. Intensity is increased as the current through the filament is increased.

Tungsten lamps are usable for temperatures up to about 3500 K. Some arc lamps operate at temperatures as high as 5500 K.

Coherent Radiation

Lasers are ideal sources of coherent radiation; that is, they emit energy at a single wavelength. Lasers generate energy by use of the electrons bound to an atom rather than by use of the free electrons created from a heated cathode. Bound electrons may be stimulated to produce the emission of energy.

Lasers are classified by the type of active medium used, such as gas, solid-state, liquid, or semiconductor.

The process of activating a laser to produce stimulated emission is called *pumping*. Gas lasers are generally pumped by an electric discharge. Solid-state lasers are usually pumped by high-intensity lamps (Fig. 5-23). Semiconductor lasers are pumped by an electric current through the semiconductor junction.

The pump energy is absorbed by the active medium, placing most of the atoms in an active state. That is, the atoms move to a higher state and create a population inversion (more atoms at a higher energy level than at a lower energy level).

Once a population inversion is reached, the atoms will give up energy rather than absorb more energy. Photons are emitted by the excited atoms as they revert back to their normal lower energy level.

Coherent radiation will be produced if the return of atoms to their normal energy level is controlled in such a way that the triggering photons are augmented by the newly emitted photons. In most lasers, the first photons emitted are used to trigger additional photons of the same energy level. The laser then becomes an oscillator. The emitted photons are enclosed in a resonant cavity with reflecting end walls. The photons are reflected back into the mass of excited atoms, triggering more photons to be released. One of the reflecting mirrors is made slightly transparent, permitting some of the oscillating photons to escape as the output laser beam.

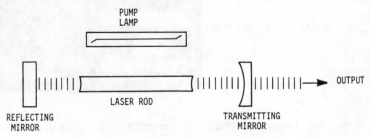

Fig. 5-23. Pumping a solid-state laser.

Most common lasers emit visible radiation in the red or blue. Neodymium-doped yttrium aluminum garnet (Nd:YAG) lasers emit energy in the near-infrared region at 1.06 micrometers. Nd:YAG lasers with continuous outputs of up to 200 watts are readily available.

Carbon-dioxide (CO_2) lasers emit energy at 10.6 micrometers and are available in continuous-wave outputs in excess of 5000 watts. Carbon-dioxide lasers are the most efficient of all lasers presently available. Typical efficiency is 10 percent; that is, 10 watts will be emitted for every 100 watts put into the laser.

COLLIMATORS

Many infrared radiometers and systems are designed to monitor or observe energy from distant targets. Ideally, calibration of an infrared system would be from a known source at the remote traget. This is usually not practical.

Courtesy Infrared Industries, Inc.
Fig. 5-24. Infrared collimator.

A collimator is used to provide a known source of infrared radiation that appears to be at infinity. The source may be a blackbody radiator, a spectral emitter, or a laser. Fig. 5-24 shows an infrared collimator.

Fig. 5-25 shows an optical schematic of a typical off-axis collimator. Off-axis collimators provide large areas of uniform intensities that are free of obstruction.

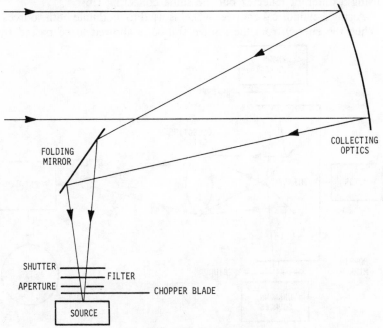

Fig. 5-25. Off-axis collimator.

An adjustable aperture is located at the focal point of the optical system. The infrared source (blackbody, tungsten lamp, etc.) is placed just beyond the aperture. A fixed- or variable-frequency chopper blade and a filter wheel may be included. The collimator may also contain an optical shutter. Typical collimators have 6- to 12-inch-diameter exit apertures.

Collimators may be entirely reflective, entirely refractive, or a combination of both. Any one of the optical systems described in Chapter 3 may be used.

Comparators

An infrared comparator is used to compare a known or standard source of infrared energy to an unknown. It is particularly useful for calibrating or checking the accuracy of secondary standards.

A simplified schematic of a typical infrared comparator is shown in Fig. 5-26. The optical paths of the known and unknown sources must be symmetrical. The accuracy of the comparator increases as the use of optical components decreases, or as the amount the components can be shared by both optical paths increases.

The known radiation source is reflected by a front-surfaced mirror through a collecting lens and focused onto an infrared detector. The unknown source is also directed to the detector in the same manner, using a different reflector but the same collecting lens.

A single cylindrical chopper wheel is used to modulate both sources. When the energy from the known source is allowed to be passed by

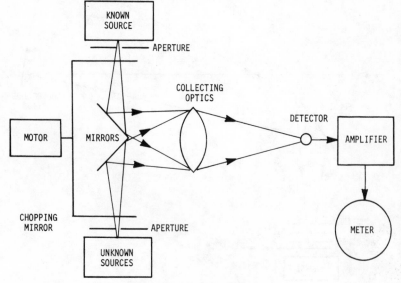

Fig. 5-26. Infrared comparator.

the chopper, the energy from the unknown is blocked by the opposite end of the cylindrical modulator. This permits the detector to "look" alternately at each source.

If both sources are equal in energy then the detector will not produce an ac signal. The amplitude of any ac signal generated by the detector will increase as the difference in energy levels between the two sources increases.

In actual use, the energy output of the unknown source is increased (or decreased) until the comparator indicates a null or zero output. At this time the unknown source is generating an output equal to the known source.

Once a null is reached it is advisable to interchange the sources and double check for a null. This interchange eliminates any possibility of error due to nonsymmetrical optical paths that may be caused by misalignment, dirty optics, or different-size apertures.

Modulators

Modulators are used to "chop" infrared energy into pulses that can more easily be recognized and measured. Energy modulators may be fixed or variable in frequency and may be used with infrared receivers or transmitters. The most common type of modulator uses a motor-driven rotating disc having a serrated edge or series of holes.

Square-wave modulation is obtained when the chopper-blade opening is considerably larger than the optical beam being modulated. Sinusoidal modulation is achieved when the chopper blade opening is equal to the diameter of the optical beam. Tuning forks may also be used as infrared modulators.

Electro-optical and acousto-optical modulators are also used with infrared systems. These modulators are generally made of a transmitting material that changes its index of refraction when subjected to electrical or acoustical variations.

Fig. 5-27. Electro-optical modulator.

95

Since these modulators are dependent on changes in index of refraction they are ideally suited for monochromatic or coherent energy.

The electro-optical modulator shown in Fig. 5-27 is an amplitude modulator made of potassium dihydrogen phosphate (KDP) and can modulate near-infrared energy from dc to 50 megahertz. Phase and frequency modulation can also be obtained.

SPECTROSCOPES

A spectroscope is an optical instrument which produces a complete spectrum by separating light or infrared radiation into individual wavelengths. The spectroscope may use prisms, gratings, or interferometers to produce the spectral separation. Prisms provide wavelength separation by refractive dispersion, while gratings work by diffractive dispersion.

Prism-type spectroscopes are most common and can typically resolve wavelengths of 10^{-4} micrometers at 1.0 micrometer. Gratings provide about 10^{-5}-micrometer resolution, and interferometric techniques can provide up to 10^{-6}-micrometer resolution at 1.0 micrometers.

There are many types and variations of spectroscopes. Some are discussed in the following.

Spectrometer

A spectrometer is an instrument that measures the angular deviation of light as it passes through a prism. Wavelength is usually determined by the angular position of the prism. A dial connected to the prism base can be calibrated directly in wavelength.

Recording spectrometers automatically rotate the prism and record relative signal intensities directly onto chart paper which may be calibrated in wavelength.

Spectrophotometer

A spectrophotometer is an instrument that compares the intensity of a reference beam to the intensity of a sample beam at the same wavelengths. Fig. 5-28A shows a modern spectrophotometer, and Fig. 5-28B shows a simplified optical schematic of a typical spectrophotometer.

The infrared source is modulated at 11 hertz and deflected into two directions by the chopping mirror. The resulting reference beam and sample beam are recombined and directed to the entrance slit.

If a detector were placed at the entrance slit it would:

1. Measure no ac signal (at 11 hertz) if there were no sample or obstruction placed in the sample beam.

Courtesy Beckman Instruments, Inc.

(A) Photo.

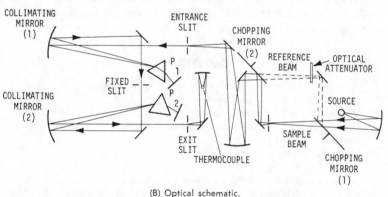

(B) Optical schematic.

Fig. 5-28. Spectrophotometer.

2. Measure a maximum ac signal if the sample beam (or the reference beam) were completely blocked.
3. Measure an ac signal with an amplitude related to optical attenuation of the sample beam.

The recombined beam is directed through a prism, P_1, where it is dispersed and reflected back through the same prism and redirected to another slit.

97

The optical components between the entrance slit and the fixed slit form a monochromator, which selects narrow portions of the spectrum. The beam is then directed through another monochromator for further dispersion. The beam is then focused onto a thermocouple.

The signal from the thermocouple is amplified and used to position the optical attenuator in the reference beam path. The optical attenuator is constantly being positioned so that the radiant energy from the reference beam is also equal to the radiant energy from the sample beam.

The position of the optical attenuator is related to the percent of transmission through the sample beam. This position is used to plot pen recordings of transmission versus wavelength. Wavelength is determined by the position of prism P_2.

Spectograph

A spectrograph is an optical instrument that photographically records the spectral lines emitted by a source. The resulting photograph, or record, is known as a *spectrogram*.

Spectroheliograph

A spectroheliograph is a special camera designed to take solar photographs. The spectroheliograph allows energy at a single wavelength to expose the film. The resulting photograph is called a *spectroheliogram*.

QUESTIONS

5-1. An infrared radiometer is an instrument:
  A. Used to monitor radio frequencies.
  B. Designed to emit infrared radiation.
  C. Used to measure the amount of infrared radiation generated by a remote object.
  D. Used to collimate infrared radiation.

5-2. A basic infrared radiometer must contain at least:
  A. An infrared detector.   C. An emissivity adjustment.
  B. A synchronous demodulator.   D. An internal reference.

5-3. What changes are necessary to increase the radiant power received by the infrared detector in a radiometer?
  A. Increase the target temperature.
  B. Decrease the focal length of the optical system.
  C. Increase the area of the detector element.
  D. All of the above.

5-4. An optical modulator (or chopping blade) is normally placed between:
  A. The target and the collecting optics.

B. The detector and the collecting optics.
C. The detector and the preamplifier.
D. The collecting optics and the internal reference.

5-5. What is the maximum chopping frequency that should be used for a detector with a time constant of 100 μs?
A. 270 Hz.   C. 1590 Hz.
B. 875 Hz.   D. 14,370 Hz.

5-6. Synchronous detection is used to:
A. Distinguish between "hot" and "cold" targets.
B. Provide automatic calibration.
C. Detect targets that do not fill the radiometer field of view.
D. Determine the chopping frequency.

5-7. A multichannel radiometer has:
A. An internal calibration source and a built-in reference.
B. More than one signal-processing channel.
C. More than one optical system.
D. More than one set of sighting optics.

5-8. A typical infrared thermometer measures remote temperatures between:
A. −100° and +100°F.   C. 200° and 5000°F.
B. 1000° and 5000°F.   D. 5000° and 10,000°F.

5-9. An optical pyrometer may be used to measure temperatures between 500° and 1000°F.
A. True.
B. False.

5-10. A two-color radiometer:
A. Measures the ratio of energy emitted by an object at two separate wavelengths.
B. Is usually painted red and blue.
C. Measures the sum of the energies emitted by an object at two separate wavelengths.
D. Is a device used to measure spectral radiant energy.

5-11. A laser is a device that emits:
A. Total radiation.   C. Coherent radiation.
B. Spectral radiation.   D. All of the above.

5-12. A collimator is used to provide a known source of infrared radiation that appears to be at infinity.
A. True.
B. False.

5-13. An infrared comparator is used to compare a known total radiation source to an unknown spectral radiant source.
   A. True.
   B. False.

5-14. A spectroscope produces spectral separation by use of:
   A. A prism.   C. An interferometer.
   B. A grating.   D. All of the above.

6

SYSTEMS

Infrared systems are available for many applications: imaging, communications, radar, temperature measurement, intrusion, gas analysis, microscopy, and detector testing. In this chapter we will examine these systems.

IMAGING

Infrared imaging systems enable a person to "see" infrared emissions. They are used to convert invisible infrared radiation into light. There are two basic types of infrared imaging systems: passive and active (Fig. 6-1).

In a passive system, only the energy emitted by a target is received, processed, and displayed. In an active system, the target is "illuminated" by an infrared "searchlight," and the reflected infrared energy is received, processed, and displayed.

Scanning infrared imaging systems may be scanned in one or two dimensions. One-dimensional scanning can produce a two-dimensional display if the target is moving or if the scanning system is moving along the target.

Passive Systems

Fig. 6-2 shows a simplified diagram of a two-dimensional scanning infrared imaging system. The scanning mirrors are panned in vertical and horizontal motions. Rapid scanning is used in one dimension while a slow scan is used in the other dimension, producing a single-frame raster that takes from a few seconds to many minutes, depending on the need. In some systems a single mirror may be used.

Total scan coverage and resolution are expressed in angular units. At a given distance from the scanning system, the height and width of the scanned area are

$$H = d\theta_r \qquad (6\text{-}1)$$
$$W = d\theta_h \qquad (6\text{-}2)$$

where,
H equals height of scan,
W equals width of scan,
d equals distance from mirror to target,
θ_r equals total vertical scan angle in radians,
θ_h equals total horizontal scan angle in radians.

Example—How large an area would be scanned by an imaging system that has a vertical scan angle of 15° (0.262 radian) and a horizontal scan angle of 20° (0.35 radian) at a distance of 60 inches?
Answer—From Equations 6-1 and 6-2,

$$H = 60\ (0.262) = 15.72 \text{ inches high}$$
$$W = 60\ (0.35)\ \ = 21 \text{ inches wide}$$

The number of resolution elements along a scan line is

$$N_e = \frac{\theta}{\alpha} \qquad (6\text{-}3)$$

where,
N_e equals number of resolution elements,
θ equals total scan angle,
α equals instantaneous optical resolution angle (field of view).

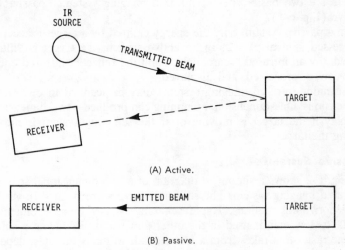

(A) Active.

(B) Passive.

Fig. 6-1. Infrared imaging.

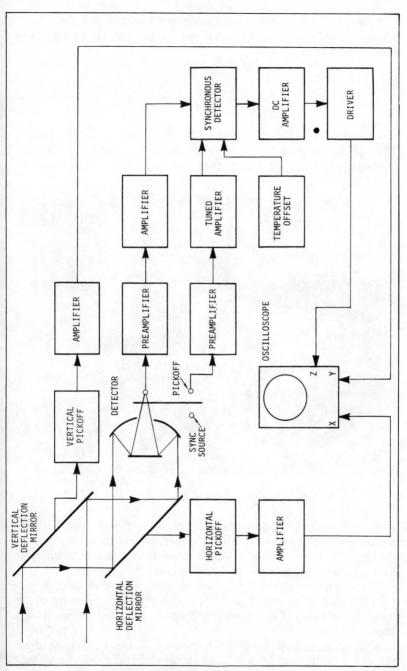

Fig. 6-2. Two-dimensional scanning system.

103

Example—How many optical resolution elements are there for a scanned system that has 15° total scan angle and an instantaneous field of view of 0.15°?

Answer—From Equation 6-3,

$$N_e = \frac{15}{0.15} = 100$$

For a total raster scan of 15° × 20° there will be 13,300 (100 × 133) resolution elements. This means that a 1-second frame time requires the need for a detector having at least a 13,300-Hz response.

Fig. 6-3. Infrared scanning camera and display.

An indium antimonide detector with a time constant of 1 microsecond can easily resolve 13,300 elements in less than 1 second. A thermistor bolometer with a 1-millisecond time constant requires at least 13.3 seconds to scan 13,300 elements.

The target being scanned is focused onto a detector and the resultant signal is amplified and used to control the intensity of an oscilloscope beam. The stronger the signal, the more intense is the beam.

A position pickoff from the horizontal mirror is used to drive the x axis of the oscilloscope, and another pickoff from the vertical mirror is used to drive the y axis of the oscilloscope. The resulting picture is a thermograph of the object being observed. Black-to-white contrasts may represent temperature changes as small as 1°C or as high as 100°C, depending on the gain of the system, which is usually adjustable. Fig. 6-3 shows a modern infrared passive scanning system.

The thermograph may be recorded directly on film. In this case, the thermal signal is used to vary the intensity of a glow modulator tube. The light from the glow modulator is directed to expose the film. Scanning of the glow modulator beam is achieved by use of the system's scanning mirrors to ensure proper horizontal and vertical scan synchronization.

Active Systems

An active imaging system requires use of an illuminator to obtain the desired signal. The snooperscope and sniperscope of World War II fame are examples of active imaging. Fig. 6-4 shows a simplified optical diagram of a snooperscope system.

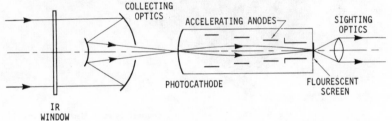

Fig. 6-4. Snooperscope system.

The illuminator is simply a high-intensity light source filtered to emit only infrared wavelengths. The invisible beam of infrared radiation is reflected back by the target and focused onto the semitransparent photocathode of an image converter tube. The photocathode then emits electrons in proportion to the amount of infrared radiation incident on its surface. The electrons are directed to the fluorescent screen, which produces an illuminated "picture" of the infrared energy striking the photocathode. The greenish picture presentation is viewed through a set of sighting optics.

The infrared laser offers a more efficient and highly directional beam for use as an illuminator. Fig. 6-5 shows a photograph of an infrared illuminator using an Nd:YAG laser that emits radiation at 1.06 micrometers.

The small-diameter output of the laser is directed through a collimating lens that provides a larger-diameter beam to be projected onto the target. The receiver for this type of illuminator may be an image converter tube or a radiometer, depending on sensitivity required, resolution, speed of response, and other variables.

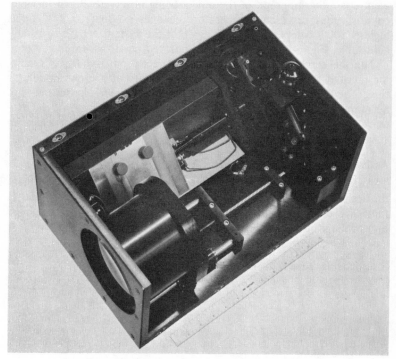

Courtesy Sylvania Electric Products, Inc.

Fig. 6-5. Infrared illuminator.

COMMUNICATIONS

Infrared techniques may be used for secure, line-of-sight communications. A simple, short-range infrared walkie-talkie system is shown in Fig. 6-6.

The user speaks into a microphone consisting of a stretched plastic diaphragm coated with a reflecting surface. Collimated light from a flashlight is reflected from the diaphragm to the receiver. An infrared filter is used to eliminate the transmission of visible energy. Sound waves reaching the diaphragm cause the reflected signal to vary its angle of divergence, which in turn affects the amount of watts per square centimeter being transmitted at any given angle.

The receiving section contains a flashlight reflector with an infrared detector in place of the lamp. The signal from the detector is amplified and used to drive a speaker or headphones.

A more practical infrared communications system using a laser is shown in Fig. 6-7. The information to be transmitted is amplified and used to drive an electro-optical modulator made of gallium

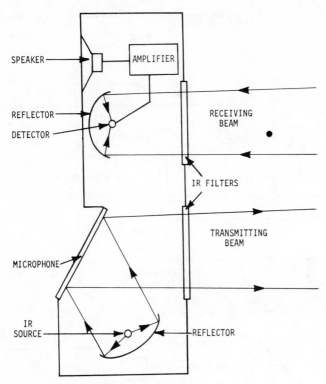

Fig. 6-6. Infrared walkie-talkie.

arsenide (GaAs). The GaAs modulator varies the intensity of the 10.6-μm CO_2 laser output. The amplitude-modulated output is directed through a telescope toward the receiver.

At the receiver (Fig. 6-7B) the 10.6-μm signal is collected and focused onto an infrared detector. The signal is then amplified and used as required.

Infrared communications systems using lasers may be amplitude modulated (a-m), phase or frequency modulated (fm), or pulse-code modulated (pcm).

In general, infrared communication systems are lighter and require less power to operate than similar radio-frequency communication systems. Infrared communications are well suited for space applications where atmospheric attenuation does not exist.

An infrared communication system is theoretically capable of transmitting 7.5×10^9 voice channels (each 4 KHz wide) or 5×10^6 video channels (each 6 MHz wide) at 10.6 micrometers. Optical modulators and detectors are not now available that will permit anywhere near the theoretical number of channels that may be used.

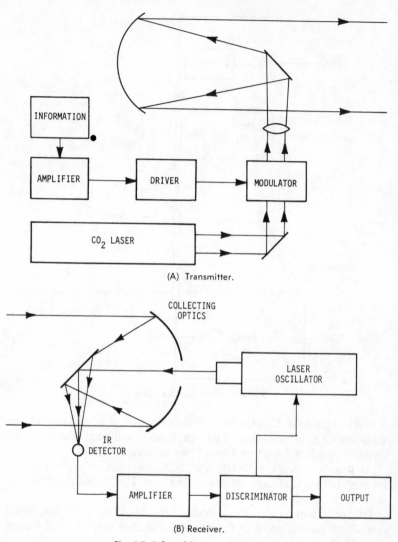

(A) Transmitter.

(B) Receiver.

Fig. 6-7. Infrared laser communications.

Radar

Radar techniques require the generation of a short pulse of energy and the measurement of time until the reflected signal is received.

We learned in Chapter 1 that light travels at 3×10^8 meters per second (or 1 mile in 5.37 microseconds). Let's assume that we have a target at a distance of 1 mile. Fig. 6-8A shows a pulse on an oscilloscope display as the signal is transmitted toward the target.

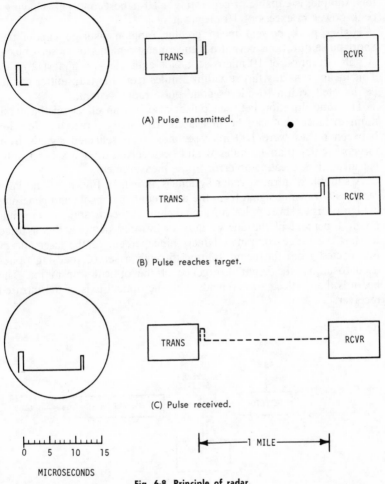

(A) Pulse transmitted.

(B) Pulse reaches target.

(C) Pulse received.

|←——————1 MILE——————→|

0   5   10   15
MICROSECONDS

Fig. 6-8. Principle of radar.

The vertical grids on the oscilloscope screen are calibrated in microseconds. Fig. 6-8B shows a time elapse of 5.37 microseconds from the generation of the pulse until the beam of energy reaches the target.

The reflected signal is received 5.37 microseconds after it is reflected back from the target (Fig. 6-8C). The total elapsed time is 10.74 microseconds (equivalent to 2 miles). Since the transmitted pulse makes a "round trip" the measured distance must be divided, by 2, to obtain actual distance.

Infrared lasers are ideal generators of very short, high-peak-power pulses that are needed for infrared radar systems. The Nd:YAG laser, for example, is capable of generating a 10-nanosecond pulse having a peak power in excess of 10 megawatts.

Higher peak powers mean greater range-measuring capabilities. Short pulse durations permit distance measurements of closer objects. A pulse duration of 10 microseconds is equivalent to almost 2 miles. This means that any target within 2 miles from the transmitter cannot be detected with a 10-microsecond pulse radar system.

The time duration between pulses also has an effect on the maximum distance that can be measured. If, for example, the duration between pulses were 100 microseconds, then reflected signals from targets greater than 10 miles would be received after a second pulse is transmitted, creating an error in the measurement.

A simplified infrared radar system is shown in Fig. 6-9. The laser receives a transmit signal from the main control console and generates a high-energy, short-pulse infrared beam. A beam splitter transmits about 1 percent of the energy into an infrared detector that is used to start the range computer. Ninety-nine percent of the laser energy is reflected from the beam splitter through a set of focusing optics used to adjust the beam divergence of the optical transmitter. The beam is then reflected to coincide with the optical axis of the infrared receiver.

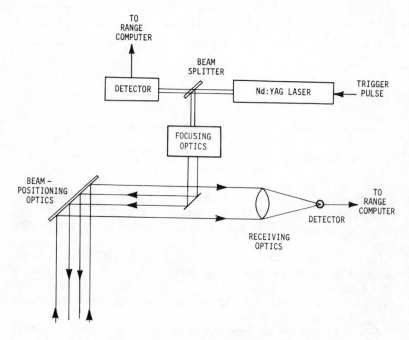

Fig. 6-9. Infrared radar system.

Horizontal and vertical beam-positioning optics are used to direct the infrared radar to a desired location.

The reflected signal is received and focused onto an infrared detector that is used to "turn off" the range computer. The elapsed time stored in the range computer may be read out in time or distance (feet, yards, meters, miles).

TEMPERATURE MEASUREMENT AND CONTROL

Infrared techniques provide a means of noncontact temperature measurement and control that does not influence or contaminate the temperature of the object being measured. A typical infrared temperature measurement and control system is shown in Fig. 6-10.

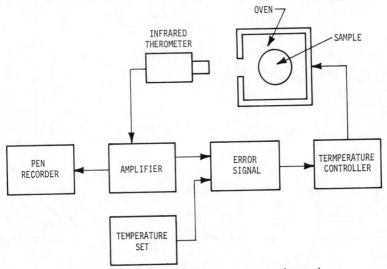

Fig. 6-10. Infrared temperature measurement and control.

The object is placed inside a furnace and its temperature is continuously monitored by the infrared thermometer. The desired temperature is set at the control console.

The temperature controller provides power to the oven's heating elements and the object starts to increase in temperature. As the temperature approaches its desired level, the thermometer output starts to null the temperature set voltage level and the resultant error signal directs the temperature controller to reduce the power to the heating elements.

If the thermometer senses a temperature higher than desired, the error signal will completely turn off the oven. Temperature control of less than 0.1 percent can be obtained by this technique.

INTRUSION

Infrared intrusion systems are used in lieu of photoelectric relays where a higher degree of secrecy is desired.

The most common type of intrusion system works by interrupting the infrared beam generated by a transmitter and monitored by a receiver. (Fig. 6-11A). The receiver activates a relay when the beam

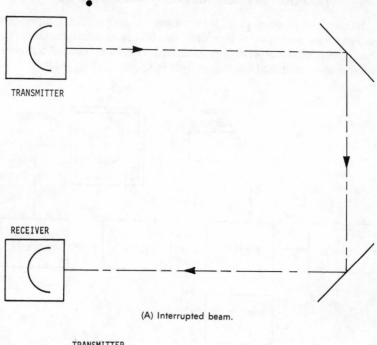

(A) Interrupted beam.

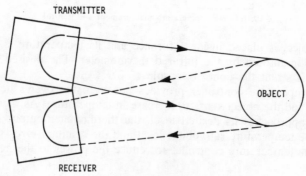

(B) Reflected beam.

Fig. 6-11. Infrared intrusion systems.

is "blocked" for any reason. The relay may be used to trigger an alarm, activate a camera, turn on a searchlight, lock a gate, or any one of a number of desired requirements.

The system shown in Fig. 6-11B is activated when an object enters a specified area and reflects the infrared signal back to the receiver. This type of system normally uses a modulated light source and a "tuned" receiver.

Use of a receiver tuned to the modulation frequency prevents the activation of a false alarm from a distant flashlight, automobile headlights, or rising sun.

GAS ANALYZERS

A characteristic of most gases is that they absorb infrared energy at specific or many wavelengths. Fig. 6-12 shows the transmission versus wavelength characteristics of six gases. It is easy to observe that if one wanted to detect the presence of benzene over the other five gases he would monitor the attenuation of an infrared source at 3.3 micrometers.

A simplified gas analyzer is shown in Fig. 6-13. An infrared source is directed through a gas chamber to an infrared detector. A filter is used to restrict the wavelength being monitored.

The detector output is used to deflect a meter that is set at full scale (100 percent) when no gas is in the chamber. When a gas having an absorption band at the wavelength being monitored is introduced into the chamber, a decrease in the detector signal output will cause the meter to indicate something less than full scale. The decrease in meter deflection is directly related to the percent transmission of the gas at the wavelength used.

Dual wavelengths (two-color) may be used to help further distinguish gases that may have common absorption bands. For example, of the six gases shown in Fig. 6-11 it may be desirable to detect the presence of carbon dioxide. It can be seen that the infrared-energy absorption at 4.3 micrometers can be used to detect the presence of carbon dioxide.

Further examination, however, shows that carbon disulphide also absorbs energy at 4.3 micrometers. The 2.7-micrometer absorption band of carbon dioxide also coincides with the 2.7-micrometer absorption band of water vapor.

In this instance both wavelengths (2.7 and 4.3 micrometers) should be monitored. The presence of carbon dioxide will cause attenuation at both wavelengths. Attenuation at 2.7 micrometers and not at 4.3 micrometers will indicate the presence of water vapor. Also, attenuation at 4.3 micrometers and not at 2.7 micrometers will indicate the presence of carbon disulphide.

113

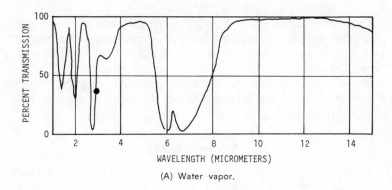

(A) Water vapor.

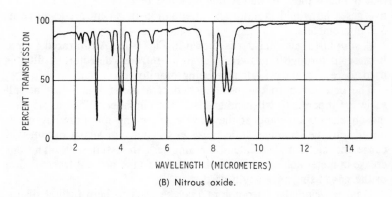

(B) Nitrous oxide.

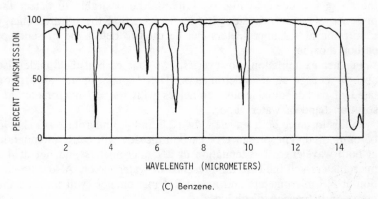

(C) Benzene.

Fig. 6-12. Infrared transmission

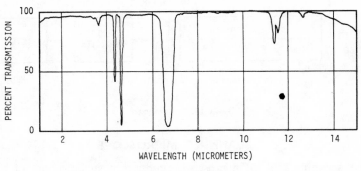

(D) Carbon disulphide.

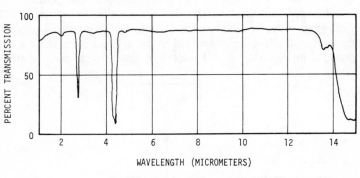

(E) Carbon dioxide.

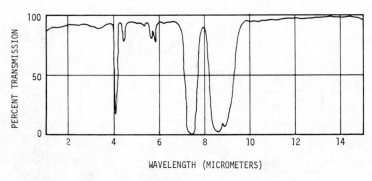

(F) Sulphur dioxide.

characteristics of gases.

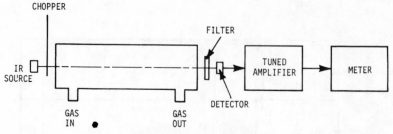

Fig. 6-13. Gas analyzer.

SCANNING MICROSCOPE

A scanning infrared microscope produces a shadowgraph of the infrared transmission of the material under examination. Fig. 6-14 shows a simplified schematic of a scanning infrared microscope.

The helium-neon laser is used to generate a 3.39-micrometer beam that is focused and directed through the sample being tested. The vertical scan mirror is nutated at a speed of about one cycle in 2 seconds. A potentiometer connected to the vertical drive shaft is used to produce an electrical signal related to the vertical position of the

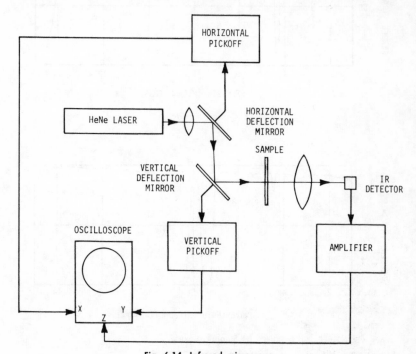

Fig. 6-14. Infrared microscope.

mirror. This electrical signal is fed to the vertical (y axis) input of an oscilloscope.

The horizontal mirror vibrates at about 200 hertz. The voltage used to drive the torsional vibrating mirror is also used to drive the horizontal (x axis) input of the oscilloscope.

The system scans an area of about 0.5 inch by 0.5 inch in one second. Spot resolution is about 0.01 inch. Details as small as 0.003 inch may be observed.

The wide-area detector generates an electrical signal that is proportional to the transmission of the laser beam through the sample. The electrical signal from the detector is fed to the intensity modulation (z axis) input of the oscilloscope. The resultant shadowgraph is a visual two-dimensional presentation of the infrared transmission characteristics of the sample.

DETECTOR TEST SET

The growing demand for infrared detectors has created a need for improved production techniques for fast, reliable quality control. Detector test sets have been developed that quickly and accurately check and record all of the important operating parameters of an infrared detector.

A block diagram of the components needed to make up a typical detector test set is shown in Fig. 6-15. A detector test set of this type can measure or determine:

1. Cell resistance.
2. Signal.
3. Noise.
4. Signal-to-noise ratio.
5. Optimum bias.
6. Responsivity.
7. NEI.
8. NEP.
9. D^*.
10. Frequency response.
11. Spectral response.
12. Noise spectra.
13. Dynamic impedance.

The blackbody radiation source is usually adjustable up to at least 1000°C. A high-intensity tungsten lamp or other infrared source may be interchanged with the blackbody source, depending on spectral and intensity requirements at the detector.

A variable-speed modulator (up to 10 KHz) chops the blackbody radiation for ease of signal handling and to measure the detector frequency response. Spectral response is determined by use of a circular variable filter.

The detector output is amplified and its signal is indicated on a voltmeter. The bias (if required) is varied while observing the maximum detector signal to provide optimum bias.

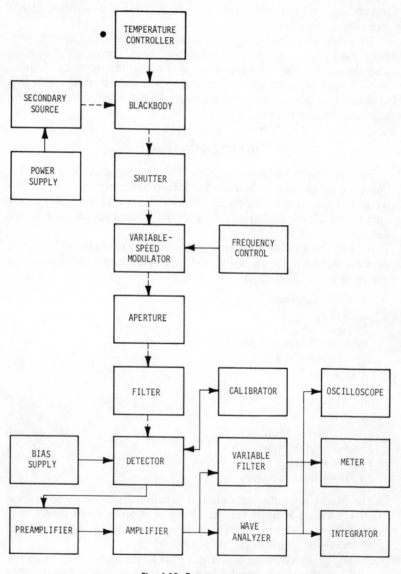

Fig. 6-15. Detector test set.

The detector output, with no infrared signal, is channeled through a narrow-band wave analyzer to measure the noise spectra of the infrared detector. A variable-bandwidth filter is also used for the measurement of detector noise.

A single-valued nonambiguous noise measurement is ensured by use of an integrator that eliminates operator reading dependency.

The cell compartment may be varied in temperature to plot cell temperature versus responsivity curves. An oscilloscope is used to monitor the detector output for signal and noise characteristics; one is visible at the upper left-hand corner of the detector measurement console of Fig. 6-16.

Courtesy Infrared Industries, Inc.

Fig. 6-16. Infrared detector test set.

QUESTIONS

6-1. An infrared imaging system converts:
  A. Light to infrared energy.
  B. Infrared radiation to light.
  C. Infrared radiation to invisible light.
  D. None of the above.

6-2. The two types of imaging systems are:
  A. Inactive and active.
  B. Visible and infrared.
  C. Active and passive.
  D. Direct and indirect.

6-3. How many optical resolution elements are there for an infrared imaging system that has a 10° total scan angle and a 0.2° instantaneous field of view?
  A. 5.
  B. 50.
  C. 500.
  D. 5000.

6-4. A thermograph is:
  A. A photograph of an infrared scanner.
  B. A passive infrared scanning system.
  C. An infrared picture.
  D. A plot of temperature versus wavelength.

6-5. The snooperscope is an example of:
  A. An active imaging system.
  B. A passive imaging system.
  C. A communication system.
  D. An optical radar system.

6-6. Infrared techniques may be used for line-of-sight communications.
  A. True.
  B. False.

6-7. Infrared communication systems may be:
  A. Amplitude modulated.
  B. Frequency modulated.
  C. Pulse-code modulated.
  D. All of the above.

6-8. An infrared communications system is theoretically capable of transmitting how many voice channels (each 4 KHz wide)?
  A. 6.5×10^5.
  B. 9.3×10^8.
  C. 7.5×10^9.
  D. 1.6×10^{15}.

6-9. How long does it take for light to travel 1 mile?
  A. 5.37 milliseconds.
  B. 5.37 microseconds.
  C. 5.37 seconds.
  D. 5.37 minutes.

6-10. Why are infrared lasers ideal transmitters for optical radar systems?
  A. They can generate very short, high-peak-power pulses.
  B. They can generate very long, high-peak-power pulses.
  C. They can generate very long, low-peak-power pulses.
  D. They can generate very short, low-peak-power pulses.

6-11. Infrared temperature measurement:
  A. Is remote.
  B. Does not require contact with the object.
  C. Does not contaminate the object.
  D. Is all of the above.

6-12. Infrared gas analyzers work on the theory that:
  A. Most gases absorb energy at specific wavelengths.
  B. Most gases absorb energy at the same wavelength.
  C. Most gases do not absorb any infrared energy.
  D. Most gases absorb energy at all wavelengths.

6-13. A detector test set is used to:
  A. Only measure the physical dimensions of an infrared detector.
  B. Measure most of the operating parameters of an infrared detector.
  C. Only measure the noise spectra of an infrared detector.
  D. Only measure the spectral characteristics of an infrared detector.

INFRARED APPLICATIONS

New applications of infrared technology are being discovered daily. This chapter deals with major applications already in use. The latter will show that the future of infrared promises to be more exciting and rewarding than the past.

TEMPERATURE MEASUREMENT AND CONTROL

Temperature measurement and control by infrared techniques is used in virtually every industrial process. Infrared radiometers provide quick, remote temperature measurement without affecting the temperature of the object being observed (Fig. 7-1).

Operation of the radiometer is simple. Just aim the unit, like a camera, and read the temperature. Most radiometers have an emissivity adjustment for absolute temperature readings. Radiometers generally have a recorder output for pen recorders or for temperature controllers.

Thanks to noncontact infrared techniques, many temperature applications considered impossible years ago are now a reality. Usually, infrared thermometers are restricted to measurement of opaque surfaces. However, special combinations of electro-optical components provide a means of noncontact temperature measurement of many transparent materials.

Normally, when an infrared thermometer observes a transparent object it not only senses the infrared energy emitted by that object, but the energy emitted by the surface directly behind it. The resultant integrated temperature will be different from that of the transparent object.

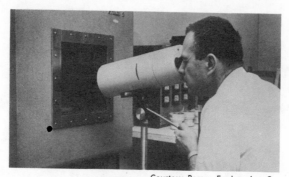

Fig. 7-1. Infrared research thermometer being used to study samples in temperature-controlled chamber.

Glass

Glass does not emit infrared energy uniformly at all wavelengths. It is desirable, therefore, to measure the radiant energy only at the longer wavelengths, beyond 4.5 micrometers, to determine glass temperatures accurately.

Most optical pyrometers operate at 0.65 micrometer, where glass is highly transparent. Some infrared thermometers look only at wavelengths shorter than 4.5 micrometers, while others look at wavelengths above and below 4.5 micrometers, giving false glass temperature indications.

Special interference filters allow observation of infrared radiation at wavelengths beyond 4.5 micrometers. By combining the proper interference filter with a long-wavelength infrared detector, glass temperature variations of 0.2 percent which occur for short durations can be detected and recorded. One-percent accuracy is possible with careful calibration techniques.

There is essentially no transmission of infrared energy through glass beyond 4.5 micrometers. This means hot sources, such as ovens, behind the glass cannot influence the temperature reading in any way.

Flame

When hydrocarbon fuels are burned in the atmosphere or with oxygen, two of the combustion products produced are water vapor (H_2O) and carbon dioxide (CO_2). Both of these products emit energy in the infrared spectrum: H_2O at 2.7 micrometers and CO_2 at 4.45 micrometers. The width of the emission band depends somewhat on the temperature and pressure at which the exhaust gases escape. Also, the transmission of the flame depends on its thickness.

Thermocouples are impractical for flame temperature measurement because of the extremely high temperatures and relatively fast contamination of the thermocouple itself.

Optical techniques offer a distinct advantage by permitting temperature measurement without disturbing the combustion process or influencing the temperature in any way. Unfortunately, many standard optical techniques are not practical because of the high transmission characteristics of flames and exhausts.

Fig. 2-10 showed the emission characteristics of a natural gas flame. Since the CO_2 band emits the strongest it is most desirable to work in this region.

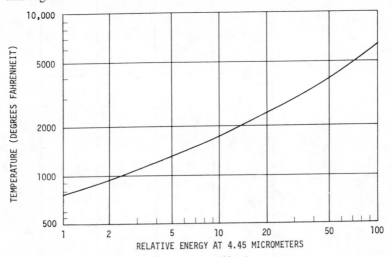

Fig. 7-2. Monochromatic calibration curve.

Fig. 7-2 shows a theoretical calibration curve for a monochromatic infrared thermometer operating at 4.45 micrometers. The curve is computed from blackbody distribution curves. Corrections to the curve should be made for flames having an emissivity value of less than one.

Calculations indicate that most flames greater than 15 inches in depth will have an emissivity value approaching unity.

Plastics

Plastics such as polyethylene may be measured at 3.5 micrometers or by use of a total infrared thermometer and blackbody radiation source.

Use of the blackbody is more applicable for control applications. Varying thickness or changes in the infrared transmission of the transparent material will not affect the control accuracy.

Let's assume that we want to control the temperature of polyethylene during extrusion and that the temperature must be maintained at 200°F. Fig. 7-3 indicates the total effective emissivity values of polyethylene at different thicknesses. Fig. 7-4 shows a typical geometrical

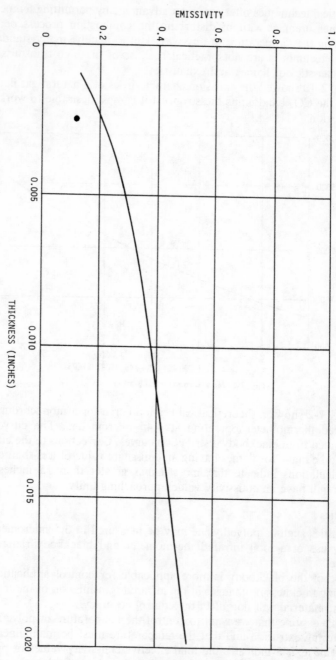

Fig. 7-3. Emissivity of polyethylene (1-7 μm).

124

layout of our application. In order to maintain a temperature of 200°F at point A, the blackbody source must be set for 200°F and the infrared thermometer sighted into its cavity.

The infrared thermometer has a voltage output (V_0) that is related to object temperature (T) in the following way:

$$V_0 = \epsilon k T^3 \qquad (7\text{-}1)$$

where k is a constant that takes into account the optical and electronic gain of the infrared thermometer, the attentuation of energy through the lenses and filter, the responsivity of the infrared detector, and the Stefan-Boltzmann constant.

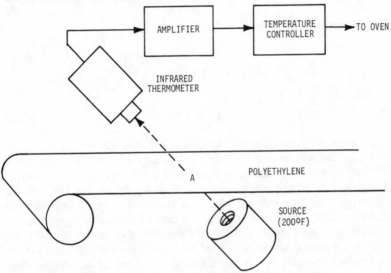

Fig. 7-4. Layout to control polyethylene temperature.

Assuming the use of an indium antimonide detector, the voltage output (V_0) is related to the third power of absolute temperature (T) because of the spectral response (1.0 to 7.0 micrometers).

With nothing between the infrared thermometer and the blackbody, let us assume that 1.0 volt will be transmitted to the controller, indicating the proper control temperature of 200°F. The voltage will of course increase or decrease as the blackbody source varies. For our application, however, we will suppose that the blackbody source will remain constant.

Next, let us place a sheet of 5-mil polyethylene as shown in Fig. 7-4. The polyethylene has an emissivity value of 0.3 in the spectral region used and is also at 200°F. The voltage now generated by the infrared thermometer is also equal to 1.0 volt. This can be shown mathematically as

$$V_0 = \epsilon_p k T_p{}^3 + \tau_p(\epsilon_{bb} k T_{bb}{}^3) \qquad (7\text{-}2)$$

where,

ϵ_p equals emissivity value of the polyethylene,
T_p equals absolute temperature of the polyethylene,
τ_p equals transmission factor of the polyethylene,
ϵ_{bb} equals emissivity value of the blackbody,
T_{bb} equals absolute temperature of the blackbody (equal to T_p).

By definition, the emissivity factor of a blackbody is 1.0. Also, neglecting reflectivity,

$$\tau = 1 - \epsilon \qquad (7\text{-}3)$$

and by substitution Equation 7-2 becomes

$$V_0 = \epsilon_p k T_p{}^3 + (1 - \epsilon_p) k T_{bb}{}^3$$
$$= \epsilon_p k T_p{}^3 + k T_{bb}{}^3 - \epsilon_p k T_{bb}{}^3$$

Since $T_{bb} = T_p$,

$$V_0 = k T^3 \qquad (7\text{-}4)$$

As shown by the preceding equations, the transmission factor of the polyethylene has no effect on the voltage output when the temperature of the transparent material is equal to the temperature of the black-body. Since transmission is determined mostly by the thickness of the material, thickness will not affect the control voltage in any way. In actual practice the source is set at the desired control temperature.

The voltage output will not follow the theoretical temperature curves for temperatures above or below the desired set point. However, the controller is not interested in the accuracy of temperatures above or below its set point. An error voltage related to the offset temperature will provide the controller with reliable control temperature information.

NONDESTRUCTIVE TESTING

Infrared techniques may be used for many applications requiring remote, nondestructive testing. Some common uses are to:

1. Identify semiconductors that have been damaged by overheating during soldering.
2. Analyze electronic circuit performance, during operation, without disturbing the circuit. (See Fig. 7-5.)
3. Detect overrated or underrated components in electrical circuits.
4. Detect cold solder connections.

5. Predict component failure or shortened life time.
6. Check bridge wire reliability without destroying or touching the wire.
7. Point out poor bonds.
8. Determine combustion efficiencies of engines.
9. Measure engine thrust by analyzing exhaust gases.
10. Predict blowouts in rubber tires.
11. Detect "hotboxes" on railroad cars. (See Fig. 7-6.)
12. Find voids or air bubbles in solid-propellant fuels.
13. Pinpoint overheating of engines and missiles during tests.
14. Find voids in cast metals.
15. Indicate cracks in welds.
16. Measure efficiency of microwave transmissions.
17. Find stresses in glass materials.
18. Find defects in insulation.
19. Plot temperature profiles of nose cones in wind tunnel tests.

The radiometer can be used for the detection of bonding voids in solid-propellant motors. This technique utilizes the effect of bonding on thermal conductivity. Areas of good bond conduct heat more readily than poorly bonded areas. A thermal gradient will appear on the outer surface, providing an indication of the thermal conductivity of the various paths through the liner and propellant, or liner and outer case.

Fig. 7-5. Portable infrared thermometer measuring temperature of electronic components.

Courtesy Raytek, Inc.

Heating of the material may be accomplished by induction techniques or by use of infrared lamps. Heat can be applied for several minutes or thermal bursts of a few seconds may be used. The time depends on the material, its thickness, and what one hopes to observe.

Normally defects are more apparent during thermal increase or thermal decrease. Once the material is allowed to reach equilibrium, detection of flaws, cracks, voids, etc. becomes extremely difficult. Thermal bursts have the advantage of not excessively overheating the samples and causing damage.

For the detection of weld defects on large pipes, the pipe section is passed under the coils of a high-frequency generator. The radiometer is aimed at a point approximately 2 inches past the point of maximum heat. The flow of heat through the pipe and any good weld should be uniform; if not, a temperature change will be noticed.

Radiometers are ideal for remote temperature readings of inaccessible structures and materials being bombarded within a nuclear reactor. In this case, response time of a few microseconds may be desirable.

High-speed infrared radiometers may also be used for various wind-tunnel and shock-tube tests.

Pinpointing structural defects of tires rotating at speeds in excess of 100 mph is possible with infrared techniques. Blowouts on the test stand can be predicted up to 12 hours in advance.

Uniform temperatures are assured by using infrared radiometers while applying resin-impregnated fiberglas filaments, under tension, to rocket motor cases and nose cones.

Defects in power-line transmission insulators or connectors and poor splices can be detected before electrical service is interrupted or costly repairs are needed. Any resistance to the current through the transmission cable will cause power to dissipate at the point of resistance, which will cause an increase in temperature. This temperature increase can easily be detected by infrared thermometers. (See Fig. 7-7.)

It is known that the internal temperature of electronic components is a major factor affecting life time of components. Infrared scanning or thermal imaging techniques enable one to rapidly determine extremely small variations in temperature over large areas. A thermal

Courtesy Raytek, Inc.

Fig. 7-6. Measuring
junction-box temperature
on railroad car.

Courtesy Raytek, Inc.

Fig. 7-7. Measuring temperature of
high-voltage insulators with portable unit
having telescopic lens.

map is displayed on a CRT or film showing the relative temperature distribution of the material's surface.

Microradiometers can be used to measure temperatures of objects as small as 0.001 inch in diameter. This type of instrument is ideal for electronic circuit analysis.

Infrared thermometry is now playing a vital role in nondestructive testing. It is a necessary tool for every quality control laboratory in the country. New applications of infrared techniques in nondestructive testing are being born everyday. Applications are limited only by one's imagination.

Being relatively new, infrared in some applications needs more testing and correlation with other techniques. However, the day is fast approaching when no nondestructive test will be complete without infrared verification.

MEDICAL USES OF INFRARED

Infrared imaging techniques promise to enhance the already proven roles of electronics in medicine. Within a short time, infrared instrumentation will be as valuable a tool to doctors and hospitals as the X-ray machine is today.

The medical profession has used infrared photography for a number of years. This method, however, is limited by the fact that the film emulsions are sensitive primarily to reflected energy at the very near infrared wavelengths.

New thermal imaging devices detect emitted radiation and "see" farther into the infrared spectrum. These devices enable the medical examiner to observe and record skin-temperature differentials without physical contact with the patient.

Infrared scanners have been used for clinical studies in the United States, Canada, and Europe. These "cameras" have been utilized experimentally as a basic research tool for the detection of breast cancer, determining the degree of skin burns and frostbite, and for numerous other clinical studies.

Human skin at a temperature of 37°C emits more than 50 percent of its radiant energy between 5 and 14 micrometers. The maximum energy is emitted at approximately 9.3 micrometers.

The infrared emissivity of human skin, regardless of color, very closely approaches unity ($\epsilon = 1$). This one fact means that reliable, remote plotting of skin-surface temperatures can be made regardless of skin color, visible light conditions, or ambient temperatures, and it further insures a high degree of reproducibility.

It is also important to know that the heat generated by an illness or reaction must occur on or near the surface of the skin in order to be detected by infrared methods.

The term "thermography" is used to describe the technique involving infrared scanning cameras. The word "thermograph" generally is used to describe the final picture. Fig. 7-8 shows an ordinary photograph and a thermograph (Fig. 7-8B). On the thermograph, black to white represents about 1 °C.

It has been found that identical symmetrical areas of the body surface are almost always within 1 °C unless there is a derangement of the vascular supply or some pathological process to explain it.

Medical doctors have recognized that breast cancer provokes varying degrees of local inflammatory reactions associated with an increased blood and lymphatic supply. Tests show that the average temperature rise in either the area of the tumor or ipsilanteral aerola is 2.27 °F. No temperature rise has been associated with cysts or fibroadenomata.

Hundreds of cancer patients have had an infrared scanner used on them. The results, though not official, are quite significant in warranting further experimentation.

One hundred patients, each having a lump in one breast, were investigated in London, England. All cases showing a rise of more than 1 °C over the contralateral normal area were designated as "hot" while the others were "cold."

The "hot" group consisted of abscesses and cancers, while the "cold" group contained degenerative lesions, such as cysts and duct stasis. There were only four exceptions to this: Three cases of carcinoma failed to show a rise in temperature and one cyst did show a temperature increase.

The value of infrared diagnosis lies in its early detection of symptoms.

Thyroids also have been studied. It has been observed that overactive toxic goiters are extremely hot and therefore emit more infrared radiation than underactive ones.

(A) Photograph.

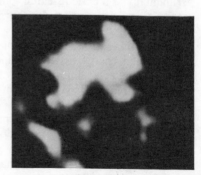
(B) Thermograph.

Fig. 7-8. Profiles.

More accurate and earlier evaluation of burn injuries can also be made by infrared techniques. Destroyed or devitalized skin limits the amount of infrared radiation emitted as compared with partially burned skin.

Healthy adult dogs have been used to test the usefulness of infrared techniques for detection of degrees of skin burns. The dogs were anesthetized, shaved, and then exposed to high-intensity heat sources for duration of 5 to 20 seconds. Fifty-five thermographs were taken periodically for up to 24 hours after injury. Positive correlation of the degree of burn was obtained in 50 of the 55 thermographs.

Twenty-seven frostbite injuries were also produced in varying degrees to the shaved dog skin. The lesions were examined and observed for seven days. In all instances the infrared scanner was reliable in predicting the onset of gangrene.

An increase in skin temperature over the appendix has been seen to occur several hours before the white blood count rose, indicating a possible use of infrared in the earlier diagnosis of appendicitis.

Since any inflammation is associated with heat and therefore has an increased infrared emission, successful treatment becomes obvious by the reduction of heat.

Infrared imaging also may be of great assistance to doctors in the study of congenital defects, vascular inflammations, drug reactions, and circulatory diseases.

The real promise of thermal imaging systems in medicine is unknown at this time. It is the job of medical research teams to interpret the significance of observable remote skin-temperature measurements and correlate this information with diagnosis based on other techniques.

MILITARY APPLICATIONS

Military uses of infrared techniques are numerous. Many are classified.

Infrared communications are ideal for military use. They are wireless, relatively compact, and very directional, which ensures private communications. Infrared communication systems were first used in World War II.

Infrared imaging systems consisting of the snooperscope and sniperscope were also used in World War II. Newer, more sophisticated imaging systems convert periscopes and telescopes for use at night; distinguish between natural and camouflaged objects; and map target areas at night.

Missile guidance is another interesting application of infrared technology. Infrared homing missiles such as the Navy's *Sidewinder* and the Air Force's *Falcon* have been operational for many years.

The guidance systems in these air-to-air missiles provide continuous target position information to constantly aim the missile on a collision course. Most airborne targets generate large amounts of infrared energy and thereby provide strong signals for the infrared-sensing missiles to "home-in" on.

Infrared radar systems are used for early warning of aircraft and ballistic missiles. Passive radar systems do not transmit signals that may be detected and indicate its position. Infrared radar systems also provide search, acquisition, and tracking information for gun fire control.

SPACE TECHNOLOGY APPLICATIONS

Infrared radiometers are used with telescopes to track the sun, moon, and stars for positioning astronomical instruments for observations and measurements. The detection and tracking of celestial objects is important for space navigation.

Satellites use the earth as a reference for position and altitude control. The carbon-dioxide layer around the earth produces a corona that makes visual observation inaccurate. Infrared radiometers operating at about 12 micrometers greatly increase the accuracy of earth horizon sensors.

The TIROS (Television and InfraRed Observation Satellite) satellite has been successfully used to plot and forecast weather conditions. Infrared surveillance of earth cloud coverage and hot air masses can aid in the forecasting of rain, snow, thunderstorms, and hurricanes.

Infrared radiometers aboard satellites have measured the surface temperature of Mars and Jupiter. The Mariner 6 satellite, for example, measured the surface temperature in the equatorial region of Mars at $+20°C$. It also observed a temperature of $-120°C$ at a latitude of $77°$ south. Infrared techniques can also aid in the evaluation of the mineral content below the surface of a distant planet.

INFRARED PHOTOGRAPHY

Near-infrared energy may be detected by photographic means. Photographic emulsions are available that allow film to "see" wavelengths as long as 1.4 micrometers. A major use for infrared film is aerial photography, since the longer wavelengths penetrate the atmospheric haze with less attenuation.

Comparison of infrared photographs with normal photographs can be used to identify certain objects or detect camouflaged items. The comparison of photographic information at two different wavelengths can yield much information concerning landscapes, paintings, and other documents.

Any camera can be used to take infrared photographs. All that is needed is some infrared film and a special filter. The filter is used to attenuate all, or most, of the visible energy striking the film.

MEASURING EMISSIVITY

The radiant emittance of most surfaces is not unity (that is, most objects are not blackbodies) and, therefore, the accuracy of temperature measurement by infrared thermometers depends on the accuracy of the emissivity factor used. This section describes practical field methods for determining the emissivity factor of an object. In most cases a relative-reading infrared thermometer with a linear meter scale is used. Direct temperature-reading infrared thermometers can be employed by using the percent of meter deflection, or by using the voltage output provided for recorder and/or controller operation. In most instances the actual temperature of the object need not be known.

Emissivity is the ratio of radiant energy emitted by a substance at a given temperature (T) to the radiant energy emitted by a blackbody at the same temperature (T). (See Equation 2-4.)

If your infrared thermometer employs an emittance control, measuring emissivity is simple: First, point the radiometer at the object. Then, determine the actual temperature by use of a thermocouple or other suitable method. Turn the emittance control until the instrument indicates the same temperature and read the emissivity value directly off the control.

Opaque Objects

There are several ways to determine the emissivity of opaque objects. We will consider four methods of doing this.

Using Blackbody Curves—Relative-reading infrared thermometers indicate a signal (W_s) directly proportional to the energy (W_o) emitted from an object, and can be employed to solve for ϵ in Equation 2-4. Fig. 7-9 shows typical calibration curves for infrared thermometers using various types of infrared detectors. These curves are for blackbody sources where ϵ is equal to 1, and can be used as arbitrary signal levels for energy.

The first step is to aim the infrared thermometer at an object whose emissivity value is unknown and observe the relative signal output (W_s). Next, determine the true temperature of the object by means of another suitable method.

Let's assume that the infrared thermometer has an indium antimonide (InSb) cell without any spectral interference filters, and further assume that the object is at a temperature of 500°C. Fig. 7-9 shows that a blackbody at that temperature will produce a relative signal of 15 (W_{bb}). Assuming further that the signal (W_s) from the

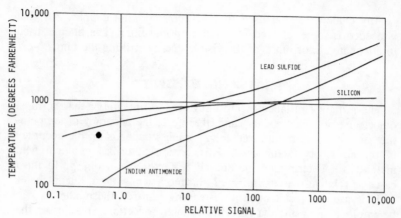

Fig. 7-9. Infrared thermometer calibration curves.

infrared thermometer is equal to 10, Equation 2-4 by substitution is now

$$\epsilon = 10/15 = 0.666$$

Thus, the emissivity factor of that particular object, at 500°C, is 0.666.

Using Reflectivity—Another method for determining the emissivity factor of an opaque object is to measure the reflectivity of the object. A blackbody or any stable high-temperature source (not necessarily a blackbody) must be used with the infrared thermometer.

Since the transmissivity of an opaque object is equal to zero, Equation 2-3 becomes

$$\epsilon = 1 - \rho \qquad (7\text{-}5)$$

where,

ϵ equals emissivity factor,
ρ equals reflectivity factor.

Example—What is the emissivity of an opaque object with reflectivity of 0.6?

Answer—From Equation 7-5,

$$\epsilon = 1 - 0.6 = 0.4$$

To determine ρ, place the known-temperature source in the reflected path of the infrared thermometer as shown in Fig. 7-10. Then use the following equation:

$$\rho = W_r/W_{bb} \qquad (7\text{-}6)$$

where,

W_r equals reflected radiant power,
W_{bb} equals radiant power emitted by a blackbody.

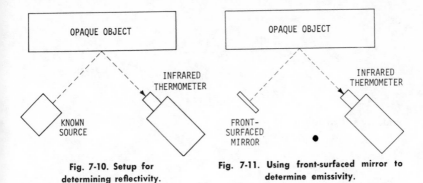

Fig. 7-10. Setup for determining reflectivity.

Fig. 7-11. Using front-surfaced mirror to determine emissivity.

By substitution in Equation 7-5,

$$\epsilon = 1 - W_r/W_{bb} \qquad (7-7)$$

It should be noted that the total power received by the infrared thermometer will equal

$$W = \epsilon\sigma T_o{}^4 + (1 - \epsilon)\sigma T_{bb}{}^4 \qquad (7-8)$$

It is important therefore to make sure that the blackbody temperature (T_{bb}) is greater than the object temperature (T_o) or that ρ is greater than ϵ to increase the accuracy of the measurement.

It should be noted that not all diffused surfaces exhibit a direct relationship between emissivity and reflectivity at all wavelengths and at all angles. If the material to be measured does not appear to have a smooth surface, a different technique should be used.

Using a Front-Surfaced Mirror—Another method, and probably the simplest, uses only a front-surfaced mirror with a relative-reading infrared thermometer.

Set the mirror in the transmitted path of a relative-temperature-reading infrared thermometer as shown in Fig. 7-11. Observe the signal output (S_1) of the infrared thermometer without the mirror:

$$S_1 = W_o \qquad (7-8)$$

where,

W_o equals the energy emitted by the object.

Next, place the mirror in position and observe the signal (S_2):

$$\begin{aligned} S_2 &= W_o + W_o\rho \qquad (7-9) \\ &= W_o + W_o(1 - \epsilon) \end{aligned}$$

Now, we can set up a proportional equation where

$$P = \frac{S_2}{S_1} \qquad (7-10)$$

135

or

$$P = \frac{W_o + W_o(1 - \epsilon)}{W_o} = 2 - \epsilon$$

or

$$\epsilon = 2 - P \qquad (7\text{-}11)$$

and, by substitution,

$$\epsilon = 2 - \frac{S_2}{S_1} \qquad (7\text{-}12)$$

Example—What is the emissivity of an object that generates a normal signal of 25 and a signal of 40 when a mirror is used as shown in Fig. 7-11?

Answer—From Equation 7-12,

$$\epsilon = 2 - \frac{40}{25} = 2 - 1.6 = 0.4$$

Making a Blackbody Out of the Object—Drilling a hole into the sample can create a blackbody condition, provided the hole is at least four times deeper than its diameter. (See Fig. 2-9).

Once the hole is drilled, sight the infrared thermometer into the cavity and observe the signal (W_{bb}). Next, reposition the infrared thermometer and observe the signal (W_s) from the surface. Emissivity can now be determined by the ratio of W_{bb} and W_s (Equation 2-4).

Transparent Objects

Most transparent objects usually have a low emissivity value because of their high transmissivity.

Use of a Front-Surfaced Mirror—One method of determining the emissivity of a transparent object also uses a front-surfaced mirror. First, take a reading as normally done with the infrared thermometer. The signal obtained will be S_1.

Now, place a mirror directly behind the object, as shown in Fig. 7-12, and measure S_2.

Neglecting reflection, the formula of Equation 7-12 can be used.

Determining Transmissivity Using a Known Energy Source—Another method for determining emissivity of transparent objects uses only a blackbody or other stable radiation source. First, observe the signal (W_{bb}) when looking directly at the source. Next, place the transparent material between the source and the infrared thermometer. The reading obtained now will be W_t.

If we neglect reflection, then

$$\tau = W_{bb}/W_t \qquad (7\text{-}13)$$

and

$$\epsilon = 1 - \tau \qquad (7\text{-}14)$$

If the reflectivity of the transparent material is high, then a combination of the methods described for opaque objects and transparent objects can be used.

Accuracies of 1 to 2 percent of emissivity can be determined by the above-mentioned techniques. Use of the front-surfaced mirror may decrease the accuracy by another 2 to 3 percent because the mirror will not be 100 percent reflective.

In many instances the emissivity value of an object may be measured at a thickness different than that used during the actual temperature measurements. In such cases, the following equation should be used:

$$\epsilon = e^{-ax} \qquad (7\text{-}15)$$

where,

e equals base of the natural logarithms,
α equals absorption coefficient,
x equals thickness of flame.

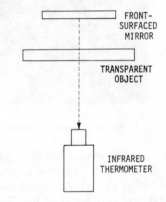

Fig. 7-12. Determining emissivity of transparent object.

MISCELLANEOUS APPLICATIONS

Infrared technology is being used in countless applications from simple radiometric measurements to complex molecular analysis. Some additional infrared applications not previously mentioned are described here. The applications described in this chapter are by no means complete.

The spectroradiometer shown in Fig. 7-13 is an analytical research tool for studies on simulated moon dust, agricultural mapping, air pollution, chemical warfare, or laboratory experiments.

Remote-sensing spectroradiometers can be used to measure the spectral radiant emissivity and reflectivity of agricultural ground cover. The output is used to identify and inventory crops, assess crop damage, and even classify soils.

Ecologists are studying the thermodynamic environment in which we live by use of infrared thermometry. Noncontact measurement permits scientists to study the heat adaptation of plants and animals in a changing thermal balance.

Schools of fish can be detected and tracked by mapping "warm" regions on the surface of oceans. It is also possible to detect and plot the flow of water pollutants in rivers and streams as well as in large bodies of water.

Courtesy Exotech, Inc.

Fig. 7-13. Spectroradiometer for field measurements.

Detection and measurement of air pollutants is another vital role that is performed by infrared instruments. Pollutants emitted by industrial plants can be monitored and recorded, day or night.

An exhaust analyzer as in Fig. 7-14 can instantly measure the percentage of carbon monoxide and parts per million of hydrocarbons emitted by the internal-combustion engine to be sure they are within federal, state and local standards. Instruments of this type can also be used for studies to increase the efficiency of internal-combustion engines.

Air turbulence has been associated with masses of warm air in the atmosphere. Aircraft using forward-looking infrared scanners can detect areas of potential air turbulence and avoid possible sudden changes in altitude and damage to the aircraft or its passengers or cargo.

Fig. 7-14. Infrared exhaust analyzer.

Courtesy Sylvania Electric Products, Inc.

Infrared reflectography has recently been developed for the study of oil paintings. Original charcoal sketches or drawings underneath the oil paintings can be detected and examined by infrared reflectivity of the painting's surface.

Infrared may also play an important role in criminology. Low light-level television cameras using near-infrared photosurfaces can be used to survey high crime areas at night without the aid of spotlights. Thermal imaging devices can tell where a car was parked or where a person sat hours after the car or person has left.

QUESTIONS

7-1. What wavelengths should be used for accurate temperature measurement of glass?
A. Wavelengths less than 1.0 micrometer.
B. Wavelengths greater than 4.5 micrometers.
C. Wavelengths between 0.65 and 3.0 micrometers.
D. Wavelengths between 1.0 and 2.0 micrometers.

7-2. Flame temperature measurements can best be made at what wavelength?
A. 0.65 micrometer.
B. 2.2 micrometers.
C. 4.45 micrometers.
D. 7.3 micrometers.

7-3. The voltage output (V_o) of an infrared radiometer may be expressed as:
A. $V_o = W_{bb}/W_b$.
B. $V_o = \epsilon k T^4$.
C. $V_o = \epsilon + T$.
D. $V_o = 1 - \epsilon$.

7-4. Infrared techniques may be used for:
  A. Predicting electronic component failure.
  B. Finding voids in solid-propellant fuels.
  C. Detecting cold-solder connections.
  D. All of the above.

7-5. Flaws that can be detected by poor thermal conduction can best be detected during an increase or decrease in temperature.
  A. True.
  B. False.

7-6. Human skin, regardless of color, has an emissivity of:
  A. Nearly 0.   C. About 0.5.
  B. About 0.3.   D. Nearly 1.0.

7-7. The *Sidewinder* is an example of:
  A. A weather satellite.   C. An infrared homing missile.
  B. An infrared communications system.   D. A snooperscope.

7-8. The TIROS is:
  A. An infrared homing missile.   C. An infrared communication system.
  B. A weather satellite.   D. An exhaust analyzer.

7-9. Infrared film emulsions are sensitive to wavelengths as long as:
  A. 1.0 micrometer.   C. 2.4 micrometers.
  B. 1.4 micrometers.   D. 5.2 micrometers.

7-10. Which of the following formulas should be used to determine the emissivity of a transparent object at a different thickness?
  A. $\epsilon = V_o k T^3$.   C. $\epsilon = 1 - \tau$.
  B. $\epsilon = e^{-ax}$.   D. $\epsilon = \alpha$.

ANSWERS TO QUESTIONS

Chapter 1

1-1. C
1-2. B
1-3. D
1-4. D
1-5. A
1-6. D
1-7. B

Chapter 2

2-1. B
2-2. C
2-3. C
2-4. D
2-5. B
2-6. A
2-7. B
2-8. B

Chapter 3

3-1. C
3-2. B
3-3. C
3-4. A
3-5. D
3-6. C
3-7. A
3-8. B
3-9. A
3-10. A

3-11. B
3-12. A
3-13. B
3-14. B
3-15. A
3-16. D
3-17. A, B, D

Chapter 4

4-1. C
4-2. B
4-3. B
4-4. C
4-5. D
4-6. A
4-7. A
4-8. A
4-9. A
4-10. C

Chapter 5

5-1. C
5-2. A
5-3. D
5-4. B
5-5. C
5-6. A
5-7. B
5-8. C
5-9. B
5-10. A

5-11. C
5-12. A
5-13. B
5-14. D

Chapter 6

6-1. B
6-2. C
6-3. B
6-4. C
6-5. A
6-6. A
6-7. D
6-8. C
6-9. B
6-10. A
6-11. D
6-12. A
6-13. B

Chapter 7

7-1. B
7-2. C
7-3. B
7-4. D
7-5. A
7-6. D
7-7. C
7-8. B
7-9. B
7-10. B

INDEX